D1442748

A SHORT GUIDE

TO

CHEMICAL LITERATURE

A SHORT GUIDE

TO

CHEMICAL LITERATURE

BY

G. MALCOLM DYSON

M. A.(Oxon.),D.Sc.,Ph.D.(Lond.),F.R.I.C.,M.I.Chem.E.

LONGMANS, GREEN AND CO

LONDON · NEW YORK · TORONTO

LONGMANS, GREEN AND CO LTD
6 & 7 Clifford Street London W 1
Thibault House Thibault Square Cape Town
605-611 Lonsdale Street Melbourne C 1
LONGMANS, GREEN AND CO INC
55 Fifth Avenue New York 3
LONGMANS, GREEN AND CO
20 Cranfield Road Toronto 16
ORIENT LONGMANS PRIVATE LTD
Calcutta Bombay Madras
Delhi Hyderabad Dacca

Second Edition © G. M. Dyson 1958

First published.... 1951
New Impression.... 1951
Second Edition 1958
New Impression.... 1960

PRINTED IN GREAT BRITAIN
BURTON PRESS LTD LOUGHBOROUGH LEICESTERSHIRE

PREFACE

The purpose of this book is to supply an introduction to the literature of chemistry, for students and research workers. Since the publication, a quarter of a century ago, by *Dr. F. A. Mason* of **An Introduction to the Literature of Chemistry**, and the issue in 1927 of **A Guide to the Literature of Chemistry** by *Drs. E. I. Crane and A. M. Patterson,* and even since the more recent publication of **The Library Guide for the Chemist** by *B. A. Soule* (1938) and **Chemical Publications** by *M. G. Mellor* (1940), there have been many changes, extensions and additions to the range of texts and journals available for chemical communications.

This book affords an introduction to the subject and has been made 'non-exhaustive' with the express purpose of keeping its price within the reach of all students of the subject; on the other hand, it is thought that no really important journal or compendium has been overlooked, and that the user will find in its pages a beginner's guide to the vast subject of chemical documentation.

I take this opportunity of thanking *Prof. H. V. A. Briscoe* for reading and constructively criticizing the draft, and *Mr. A. E. Cummins, Librarian of The Chemical Society,* for his assistance, so freely given, in settling many of the queries which have arisen during the writing of this book.

Loughborough,   G.M.D.
1951.

PREFACE TO SECOND EDITION

The opportunity of a second edition has been used to rewrite certain sections of this work, to make some necessary additions and to correct minor points overlooked in the previous version.

I would like to thank many good friends who have made suggestions for additional material, many of which have been gratefully adopted; on the other hand I would like to emphasize that in a work as small in compass as this (necessarily so, to keep its price within the compass of the student's pocket), no pretence at a complete bibliography is made; the selection of standard works are only given as *examples*.

Loughborough,   G.M.D.
1958.

TABLE OF CONTENTS

CHAPTER I.

INTRODUCTION: CHEMICAL DICTIONARIES.

THIS little book is not a bibliography of chemistry; no attempt
will be made to list the sources of chemical information in an
exhaustive fashion; the main function of the work is to indicate
to the student the general avenues of approach to the information contained in 'the literature'. In each section,
especially those relating to textbooks and technological
journals, examples only can be given, and it must be borne in
mind that these are illustrative of type; omission of a work
from the lists does not imply that it is considered less valuable
than those cited. Chemical journals have increased, both
physically and numerically, during the last three decades;
smaller print is used, and style has become more terse, so that
chemical literature, as such, now amply repays careful study.

It is becoming increasingly clear that insufficient attention
is being paid to this aspect of our work; the vast flood of
experimental data that is being poured out from the laboratories
of all nations is recorded for all to read; the chemist must
learn the paths that lead into these deep forests of information,
bearing in mind that once knowledge is 'lost' or 'buried in the
literature' the work might just as well never have been done.
The entrance to these paths is through indexes which lead us
to abstracts which, in turn, point the way to original communications; and in order to keep the plan of the terrain of chemical
knowledge clear and recognizable, this book is divided into
five main sections:-

1. General dictionaries and encyclopædias.
2. Chemical journals and periodicals.
3. Abstract journals.
4. Textbooks and special works of reference.
    4·1. History of chemistry.

1

4·2.   Analytical chemistry.
4·3.   Inorganic and physical chemistry.
4·4.   Mining and metallurgical chemistry.
4·5.   Biochemistry.
4·6.   Organic chemistry.
4·7.   Annual reviews and similar volumes.
4·8.   Applied chemistry.
5.   Some works of reference on medicinal compounds.

The fifth section is added as an example of the literature of a 'borderland' subject, linking chemistry with another of the arts or sciences.

In addition three appendixes are provided giving an account of some obsolete journals; more detailed technique of searching, and a tabular survey of the main journals with their year and volume numbers.

1. **General Dictionaries and Encyclopædias.** (This section does not include dictionaries or compendia dealing with specialized subjects, such as organic, inorganic and physical or analytical chemistry, which are discussed in the appropriate division of Section 4).

From the beginning of the nineteenth century, there developed a marked movement towards the publication of dictionaries of chemistry which attempted to describe and to classify all that was then known of the subject.   The great treatise of *Berzelius*, appearing about 1810, was the father of many such works; thus, *Gerhardt*, having been commissioned to re-edit the last French edition of *Berzelius*, found no alternative but to write a four-volume **Treatise of Organic Chemistry** which he issued in 1853.

In 1863-7, *Henry Watts* published a **Dictionary of Chemistry and the Allied Branches of other Sciences**, and this went through several editions and finally became the progenitor of **Thorpe's Dictionary.**   A second edition was published in 4 vols. (1888-94) and was reprinted several times, even as late as 1918-27.

Many of the earlier dictionaries are now only of historical interest, but the following are still of importance:-

1·11.   *O. Dammer*, **Handbuch der Chemischen Technologie.**   (5 vols. 1928-1932). This is the second edition of the original publication of 1898 giving an excellent account of the progress of chemical industry.

1·12. *O. Dammer*, **Chemische Technologie der Neuzeit** (3 vols. 1911). Gives a general outline without detail of the state of chemical invention at the period.

1·13. *H. Fehling (and others)*, **Neues Handwörterbuch der Chemie.** This compendium began publication in 1871. Although the earlier volumes are out of date, they have excellent lists of references which greatly facilitate the searching of early work. Peters and Grossman prepared a second edition in 5 vols. which was completed in 1932.

1·14. *T. E. Thorpe*, **A Dictionary of Applied Chemistry.** This valuable work was originally designed to be a companion volume to the third edition (1893) of **Watts' Dictionary of Chemistry** as set out by Muir and Morley. The latter was to contain the pure chemistry and the new compendium under *Thorpe* was to cover applied chemistry. Thorpe is now in its fourth edition, the issue of which was commenced in 1937, interrupted by the exigencies of war and completed in 1955. The work is in twelve volumes which have appeared under the auspices of an editorial board headed by *Sir Ian Heilbron*. A collective index to vols. I-V appeared in 1941 and a final complete index is in Vol. 12 (1955). This work has become a collection of small monographs on many subjects of applied chemistry and the work has been made the more useful by a liberal interpretation of the term 'applied'. Useful lists of references to original literature are given.

1·15. *J. S. Muspratt*, **Encyclopädisches Handbuch der Technischen Chemie.** 4th Edn., 11 vols. and supplements 1888-1922 (one projected supplement on 'Metals' was not published).

1·16. *J. C. Poggendorf*, **Biographisch-Literarisches Handwörterbuch.** This work is a compilation classified under the names of authors of scientific papers, with an account (bibliographical) of their contributions. It is not exclusively chemical but covers mathematics, astronomy, physics and crystallography; in addition, the volumes are of value in locating the work of investigators known only by name, and is especially useful for early work. The volumes are:-

Number	Date of issue	Period covered
1 & 2	1863	up to 1857
3	1898	1858-1883
4	1904	1884-1904
5	1926	1905-1922
6	1936	1923-1931

1·17. *F. Ullmann*, **Enzyklopädie der Technischen Chemie.** This is one of the most complete works on technical chemistry. The first edition of Ullmann appeared in 1914-1923 and the second edition in 10 volumes and an index volume was published over the period 1928-32; it was in many ways a reprint of the first edition. A third edition is now available. The work is illustrated by diagrams and flow-sheets, and has many references to technical journals and to the German Patent literature. The use of this encyclopædia is often the easiest and best introduction to a technical process.

1·18. *R. E. Kirk and D. F. Othmer (Editors)*, **Encyclopædia of Chemical Technology.** This is now complete in fifteen volumes, and one Supplement (1958).

  Vol. 1. A – Anthrimides;
  Vol. 2. Anthrone – Carbon;
  Vol. 3. Carbon (contd.) – Cinchophen;
  Vol. 4. Cineole – Dextrose;
  Vol. 5. Dialysis – Explosions;
  Vol. 6. Explosives – Furfural;
  Vol. 7. Furnaces – Iolite;
  Vol. 8. Ion exchange – Metal plating;
  Vol. 9. Metal surface treatment –
      Penicillin;
  Vol. 10. Pentacene – Polymethine dyes;
  Vol. 11. Polyols – Rutin;
  Vol. 12. Sabadine – Stilbestrol;
  Vol. 13. Stilbite – Thermochemistry;
  Vol. 14. Thermodynamics – Waterproofing;
  Vol. 15. Waxes – Zymosterol. Index.

The work has a very wide scope, and gives a good outline of the topics listed.

1·19. *H. Watts*, **A Dictionary of Chemistry.** Reference has already been made to this work (1·4).

1·20. *A. Wurtz*, **Dictionnaire de Chimie pure et appliquée.** Originally in 3 vols. (2 parts each) (1874-8); two un-dated supplemental volumes were issued, and then Wurtz and Friedel published a large supplementary treatise in 7 vols. appearing between 1892-1908. This and the previous work are now of historical value only.

1·21. *E. Fremy*, **Encyclopédie chimique.** A publication in 10 sections and 94 volumes (1882-1899). It is of historical interest only.

1·22. *Landolt-Börnstein*, **Physikalisch-chemische Tabellen.** The fifth edition of this invaluable work was published in 8 volumes between 1923-1936 and a new edition is currently appearing. Part I of Vol. 1 appeared in 1951; Part II in 1950, while Parts III, IV, V together with the 3rd, 4th and 5th volumes appeared in 1951. It gives an enormous amount of information concerning the physical properties of chemical substances. This information is considered critically, and the whole work is fully docu-mented; it constitutes one of the most important books of tables.

1·23. **International Critical Tables,** a development from the critical survey of the 1910-1923 **Tables annuelles inter-nationales de Constants et Données numeriques.** This work is issued in seven volumes, Vol. 1 being issued in 1926, and Vol. 7 in 1930. These volumes contain much critical physico-chemical data.

1·24. *A. Ladenburg*, **Handwörterbuch der Chemie.** 13 vols. (1882-1895). Now of historical interest only.

1·25. *A. Seidell*, **Solubilities of Inorganic and Organic Com-pounds.** The third edition of this work (1940) replaced the edition of 1919 which was supplemented by a subse-quent addenda volume in 1928. This work is solely a collection of data on solubilities.

1·26. *K. Kempf and F. Kutter*, **Schmelzpunkttabellen zur organi-schen Molekular Analysen.** A set of melting-point tables.

1·27. *T. E. Jordan*, **Vapor Pressure of Organic Compounds** (1954). A summary of vapour pressure data of 1150 compounds.

1·28. *R. G. Wyckoff*, **Crystal Structures.**

Part 1
Part 2 }General (1948 and 1951);

Part 3 Benzene derivatives, alicyclic and heterocyclic compounds and carbohydrates (1953)
and two supplements (1951 and 1953).

Attention must also be called to a series of year-books or handy compendia published frequently, which are useful for consultation at the laboratory bench.

Examples are:-

1·29. *J. H. Perry (Editor)*, **The Chemical Engineer's Handbook.** An invaluable book with many tables of chemical and physical properties. The third edition appeared in 1949.

1·30. **Handbook of Chemistry and Physics.** This work is published by the *Chemical Rubber Co.*, of Cleveland, Ohio, and was in its 30th Edition in 1940. It is full of useful tables and data for laboratory workers.

Various 'Chemical Dictionaries' of a smaller type have appeared from time to time; they are mainly of two types, language dictionaries for chemists and glossaries giving the meaning of chemical terms in a sentence or two.

Some examples are:-

1·31. *A. M. Patterson*, **French-English Dictionary for Chemists,** also **German-English Dictionary for Chemists.** The third, and considerably enlarged edition of the latter was issued in 1950.

1·32. *H. Bennett*, **Standard Chemical and Technical Dictionary,** published in New York in 1939.

1·33. *E. Hackh*, **A Condensed Chemical Dictionary.**

1·34. *Hoyer-Kreuter*, **Technologisches Wörterbuch.** A trilingual dictionary in English, French and German.

1·35. *G. Marolli*, **Dizionario Tecnico** (1950). A glossary of Italian technical terms.

1·36. *L. I. Callaham*, **Russian-English Technical and Chemical Dictionary.**

1·37. **The Van Nostrand Chemical Dictionary** (1953). A useful general list of technical chemical terms.

1·38. *H. Kingzett*, **Chemical Encyclopædia,** 8th Edition (1952).

1·39. *L. De Vries*, **German-English Science Dictionary.**

1·40. *L. De Vries*, **German-English Medical Dictionary.**

1·41. *M. Goldberg*, Spanish-English Chemical and Medical Dictionary.

1·42. *M. Goldberg*, English-Spanish Chemical and Medical Dictionary.

1·43. *L. L. Sell*, English-Spanish Technical Dictionary.

1·44. *L. L. Sell*, English-Portugese Comprehensive Technical Dictionary.

Among works of a general character, the following are noteworthy:-

1·45. *W. Gardner*, Chemical Synonyms, Trade-names etc., (5th Edition 1948). This volume gives a list of 28,000 words which have been accepted as 'trade-names' and is often of value in locating the nature of a material where the trade-name itself gives no indication.

1·5. Some General Works on the Literature of Chemistry.

1·51. *E. J. Crane and A. M. Patterson*, A Guide to the Literature of Chemistry (1927). Originally published in 1927; second Edition (1957) with E.M.Marr as co-author.

1·52. *B. A. Soule*, Library Guide for the Chemist (1938).

1·53. *M. G. Mellor*, Chemical Publications – their Nature and Use, 2nd Edition (1940).

1·54. *A. B. Eason*, Where to Search for Scientific Facts (1925).

1·55. *W. Ostwald*, Die chemische Literatur und die Organization der Wissenschaft (1919).

1·56. *E. E. Reed*, Introduction to Organic Research (1924).

1·57. *A. M. Patterson and L. Capell*, The Ring Index (1940). A valuable catalogue of the known rings with a system of numbering and naming them.

1·58. *A. D. Mitchell*, British Chemical Nomenclature. A valuable book for the student for it will help him towards the correct names of compounds without which a literature search cannot commence.

1·59. The *Editorial* introductions to the *Indexes* of the Journal of The Chemical Society and of Chemical Abstracts are valuable sources of information on nomenclature problems.

CHAPTER II.

CHEMICAL JOURNALS AND PERIODICALS

CHEMICAL journals and periodicals fall roughly into three classes:-

        2·1-2·2 National chemical journals.

        2·3   Specialized chemical journals.

        2·4-2·7 Ancillary and technical journals.

2·1. **National Chemical Journals.** In practically all modern civilized countries, chemical journals are maintained by the leading chemical societies. Their function is almost entirely the publication of original research and most of the important new work appears on their pages. The chief of these journals are:-

2·11. *American:* **The Journal of the American Chemical Society** and the **American Chemical Journal.** Both commenced publication in 1879; the latter became merged in the former in 1914 and since that date the J.A.C.S. has served most of the needs of America for original publication in pure chemistry.

     The **American Journal of Science,** the **Journal of the Franklin Institute** and the **Proceedings of the National Academy of Sciences** are also American Journals of the highest standing which have many papers devoted to the publication of original chemical research.

2·12. *Belgian:* The **Bulletin de la Société chimique de Belgique** has been issued since 1887, but in 1945 the name was changed to **Bulletin des Sociétés chimiques Belges;** the volume numbers, however, continue serially.

2·13. *British:* **The Journal of The Chemical Society.** This society is the oldest chemical society in existence and commenced to publish its **Memoirs** in 1841; in 1847 these became known as the **Quarterly Journal of the Chemical**

Society; in 1862, more frequent publication led to its becoming the **Journal of the Chemical Society.** In 1885 the *Chemical Society* began to publish a separate **Proceedings*** in addition to its **Journal,** in which matters of scientific interest were often discussed; this practice was abandoned in 1915 when the **Proceedings** became a record of purely business activities only. It must, therefore, be kept in mind that a reference to the **Proc. Chem. Soc.** between the years 1885 and 1914 may cover scientific material not also published in the **Journal.** In most libraries the **Journal and Proceedings of the Chemical Society** are to be found together on the shelves. In some libraries, however, the **Proceedings** are bound in at the end of the volumes entitled **Transactions.** This name arises from the fact that the **Journal** consisted for many years of two parts, **Transactions** and **Abstracts,** the former being original papers communicated to the *Society* and the latter abstracts of other chemical publications. This practice was modified in 1924 when the word **Transactions** was dropped from the title and the **Journal** became separated from the **Abstracts,** which were transferred to a special *Bureau of Abstracts.* In 1926 the volumes ceased to be numbered, the year alone constituting the full reference.

2·14. *British Commonwealth, Australian:* Apart from the **Australian Journal of Chemistry** there is no regular Australian journal specifically devoted to the publication of original chemical work, but an important review journal was commenced in 1951 - **Reviews of Pure and Applied Chemistry -** and published by the *Royal Australian Chemical Institute.* The **Australian Journal of Science, Series A, Physical Sciences,** often includes papers of chemical interest.

Canadian: The principal journals of interest to chemists are the **Canadian Chemical Journal** and the **Canadian Journal of Chemistry.**

Indian: **Journal of the Indian Chemical Society** is a

* In the first year a single volume of **Proceedings** was published (1841) and the full title during 1847 was **Memoirs and Proceedings of the Chemical Society.**

flourishing publication started in 1924 as a quarterly journal; there is, also, an **Industrial and News Edition.**
South African: The **Journal of the South African Chemical Institute** is mainly a review journal.

2.15. *Chinese:* **Journal of Chinese Chemical Science,** published up to 1946 and probably irregularly thereafter. Many Chinese chemical journals were suspended or published irregularly during the recent war years, as for example the **Transactions of the Science Society of China.**

2.16. *Czechoslovakia:* The official chemical journal of Czechoslovakia is the Chemiké Listy v. a. Premyzl.

2.17. *Danish:* A Danish Chemical Journal – the **Kongelike Danske Videnskabernes Selskab –** is published from Copenhagen.

2.18. *Dutch:* The **Recueil des Travaux Chimiques des Pays-Bas** commenced publication in 1882 and has had one anomalous year in 1917 when not only vol. 36 but part of vol. 37 was published, the latter being completed in 1918. From vol. 16 (1897) to vol. 28 (1919) the title was lengthened by 'et de la Belgique'. Originally a private venture this journal was taken over by the Dutch Chemical Society in 1920. News and review articles are published weekly in **Chemisch Weekblad,** which commenced publication in 1904.

2.19. *French:* The **Bulletin de la Société chimique de France** has been published since 1858. The first volume covers 1858 and 1859. It is a typical example of a journal published in SERIES (*i.e.* the volume numbers commence *de novo* from '1' for each series).
The series are:-

Series [1]	1858-1863	[Vols. 1-5; 1 vol. per annum]
Series [2]	1864-1888	[Vols. 1-50; 2 vols. per annum]
Series [3]	1889-1906	[Vols. 1-36; 3 vols. per annum]
Series [4]	1907-1934	[Vols. 1-56; 2 vols. per annum]
Series [5]	1935-	Since 1946 the volume number has been discontinued.

Alternate volumes are devoted to original communications and abstracts.

2·20. *German:* The **Berichte der deutschen chemischen Gesellschaft** was first published in 1868 and has steadily pursued its course of an annual volume until 1945, when publication temporarily ceased with Vol. 77 No. 11/12. Publication has been systematically resumed under the title **Chemische Berichte**, parts of which have been issued since 1947. This journal has been of paramount importance in chemical literature.

2·21. *Italian:* The **Gazzetta Chimica Italiana** has steadily issued its annual volume since 1871, when it was founded by *Paternò*. It has collective indexes for the Vols. 1-20 and 21-40.

2·22. *Japanese:* The oldest chemical journal in Japan is the **Journal of the Chemical Society of Japan** which commenced publication in 1880 and in March 1948 divided into two sections, one for Pure Chemistry and one for Industrial Chemistry. These are published monthly in Japanese and in 1927 a **Bulletin of the Chemical Society of Japan** was commenced with articles and summaries in European languages. There are also various chemical journals published by printing houses rather than Chemical Societies, such as the **Review of Physical Chemistry of Japan** and the **Journal of Japanese Chemistry**, while the **Journal of Organic Synthetic Chemistry**, is published by a Society of the same name. An excellent survey of Japanese chemical literature has been given by Stevens (J. Chem. Educ., 1954,31,471-4).

2·23. *Russian:* The older **Journal of the Russian Physical-Chemical Society** began publication in 1869 and in 1930 ceased with Vol. 62. The old journal dealt with both physics and chemistry, but the continuation of the journal in the new regimes was split into two parts, the **Journal of General Chemistry (U.S.S.R.)** and **Journal of Physical Chemistry (U.S.S.R.)**; these may also be met with under their Russian titles **Zhurnal Obschei Khimii** and **Zhurnal Fizicheskoi Khimii**. The new journal has volume numbers different from those of its older progenitor, but the older number is also cited; thus, in 1946 the legend 16/(78) indicates the two volume numbers.

The U.S.S.R. Academy of Sciences is the central publishing body of Soviet Chemical Science. The **Doklodi** (Reports) of this Academy, thirty six issues of which appear annually cover the whole of natural science. The papers are short and usually appear in a more fully descriptive form in a journal more particularly devoted to that branch of science in which the study is made.

Each section of the Academy has its own journal (**Izvestia**) which in most cases appears six times a year. In chemistry there are the following specialized journals:-

(i)   Journal of General Chemistry   Monthly
            (see above)
(ii) Journal of Applied Chemistry   Monthly
(iii) Journal of Physical Chemistry   Monthly
(iv) Journal of Analytical Chemistry   Six issues a year
(v)   Colloidal Journal   Six issues a year
(vi) Biochemistry   Six issues a year

Since 1947 the Soviet journals have discontinued the practice of giving an English or German title in addition to the Russian title. However, the translations of the titles of the twenty major Soviet journals are printed and published by the Brookhaven National Laboratory of the U.S.A.E.C. as a Guide to Russian Scientific Periodical Literature.

Review articles of chemical interest are to be found in **Uspekhi Khimiĭ** (Progress of Chemistry).

2·24. *Polish:* The official chemical journal of Poland is **Roczniki Chemiĭ.**

2·25. *Spanish:* In 1941, the **Anales de la Sociedad Española di fisica y quimica,** changed its title to **Anales de fisica y quimica.** It was first published in 1903.

2·25. *Scandinavian:* The *Swedish* chemical journal **Svensk Kemisk Tidskrift,** first published in 1889, is now (1949) in its sixtyfirst volume.

The **Acta Chimica Scandinavica,** a journal which started in 1947, is a medium for the publication of much work done in Scandinavian countries. There is also a *Finnish* journal, **Suomen Kemistilehti (Acta Chimica Fennica,** originally) which is published now somewhat irregularly from Helsinki.

2·27. *Swiss:* The **Helvetica Chimica Acta** has been issued regularly since 1918.

These are, of course, only a selection of the journals devoted to pure chemistry, and for fuller information the reader is referred to **Chemical Abstracts,** 1956, (separate publication), in which the 5236 journals abstracted by C.A. are listed (314 pp.). This list can be purchased separately and is a valuable desk book for the chemist. In addition *J. D. Stewart, M. E. Hammond* and *E. Saenger* have produced two volumes of the **British-Union Catalogue of Periodicals,** Vol. 1 (1955); Vol. 2 (1956); Vol. 3 (1957; Vol. 4 (1958). This valuable work is a record of the periodicals of the world from the 17th century to date that are available in British Libraries.

2·3. **Specialized Chemical Journals.** Specialized chemical journals may be concerned with the theoretical aspect of some branch of chemistry, or with borderland subjects. An example of the former is the **Zeitschrift für Physikalische Chemie** and of the latter, the **Biochemical Journal,** but the distinction is not very marked, and the two groups may well be considered together.

2·31. *American:* **Chemical Reviews** is a valuable medium for the publication of detailed surveys of all fields of chemical knowledge; the articles published are full and constitute an invaluable introduction to the subject treated. The reviews commenced in 1925, and two volumes a year have been forthcoming for most of the intervening period. Cumulative author and subject indexes for Vols. 1-40 are contained in Vol. 40 (1947).

The **Journal of Organic Chemistry** was inaugurated in 1936 to serve as a medium for the more spacious publication of theoretical and practical papers in organic chemistry. It is a journal which could well form part of the regular reading of an organic chemist and contains numerous contributions of importance. The **Journal of Chemical Physics** founded in 1933 and publishing a monthly number performs a similar service for physical chemistry.

The **Journal of Chemical Education** is the official organ of the *Divisions of Chemical Education* and *History of Chemistry* of the American Chemical Society and, since 1949, of the

Division of Chemical Literature; this association is reflected in its matter which is largely of historical or educational interest. It is not a usual medium for the publication of original work, but it should form part of the reading of any student of chemistry wishing to be kept in touch with recent advances and historical perspectives. A 25 year cumulative index (1924-1948) has been published.

The American Chemical Society also publishes **Industrial and Engineering Chemistry** and **Analytical Chemistry**, the latter, until 1947, being the **Analytical Edition** of the former, which, in turn, used, until 1923, to be known as the **Journal of Industrial and Engineering Chemistry**. The contents of these two journals are sufficiently indicated by their titles but it may be added that they are largely devoted to the publication of original research.

Chemical Engineering, previously known as **Chemical and Metallurgical Engineering** is a journal devoted to the purely technical side of chemical manufacture. It is useful to the non-industrial chemist for its occasional summaries of technical progress in certain fields. It started in 1902 as **Electrochemical Industry** and has changed its name four times since. The **Journal of Physical and Colloid Chemistry** was originally issued as the **Journal of Physical Chemistry**. It is an important repository of original physical chemical communications, and has been sponsored by The Chemical Society, the American Chemical Society and the Faraday Society. It was founded in 1896.

2·32. *British:* The **Transactions of the Royal Society** cannot truly be called a 'chemical journal' although many papers of great chemical significance and importance have been published in its pages. The *Royal Society* prefers to publish finished products of completed researches as distinct from short interim accounts. The publication of the **Transactions** commenced in 1665, and of the **Proceedings of the Royal Society** in 1832. The full title of the former – the **Philosophical Transactions of the Royal Society of London** gives rise to the abbreviation **Phil. Trans.** under which they are commonly cited. **Proc. Roy. Soc.** is used for the **Proceedings.**

The **Quarterly Reviews of The Chemical Society,** first published in 1947, play a part in British chemical literature somewhat similar to that played by **Chemical Reviews** in America; they afford scope for full-length surveys of chemical topics by authorities in the field concerned.

The **Transactions of the Society of Chemical Industry** constituted part of the **Journal** of that Society, and dealt with original communications on subjects of industrial and applied chemistry; the *Chemical Engineering Group* of the same Society publishes its **Proceedings,** while the Society publishes a **Journal of the Science of Food and Agriculture.** The usual reference to **J. Soc. Chem. Ind.** is to the transactions and is often particularized by a 'T' in front of the volume number. The first volume of the **J. Soc. Chem. Ind.** was published in 1882, and since 1923 the 'news' section has been published separately (weekly) as **Chemistry and Industry.** In 1951 **J. Soc. Chem. Ind.** was superseded by the **Journal of Applied Chemistry** and this now carries abstracts as well as original communications on applied chemistry. The **Proceedings of the Chemical Engineering Group of the Society of Chemical Industry** were first published in 1919. As the title suggests, they are concerned almost exclusively with chemical engineering.

The **Transactions of the Faraday Society,** first published in 1903 deal largely with the application of physical chemistry to scientific problems; they constitute part of the essential reading of those working in this field.

The scope of this journal is very wide, and many of the borderland topics of chemistry from chemotherapy to metallurgy are also exhaustively dealt with in the **Discussions of the Faraday Society** now in the seventeenth volume.

The **Philosophical Magazine (Phil. Mag.)** commenced publication in 1798 being founded by *Tilloch*; in 1814 it absorbed **Nicholson's Journal** (see Note 13, page 139) and was known as **The Philosophical Magazine and Journal.** The second series was called **The Philosophical Magazine or Annals of Chemistry, Mathematics, Astronomy, Natural History and General Science** and with the third series another change of title to **The London and Edinburgh Philosophical Magazine and Journal of Science.** The 'Dublin' was added in 1840. It was issued in Series:-

Series I	1798-1826	Vols. 1-68
Series II	1827-1831	Vols. 1-11
Series III	1832-1850	Vols. 1-37

Series IV	1851-1875	Vols. 1-50
Series V	1876-1900	Vols. 1-50
Series VI	1901-1925	Vols. 1-50
Series VII	1926-	Vols. 1-

Its later title **A Journal of Theoretical, Experimental and Applied Physics** is a sufficient indication of its main objects in publication, but much matter has appeared in its pages of interest to the physical chemist.

2.33. *French:* The **Annales de Chimie et de Physique** is the oldest chemical journal in existence: it commenced existence as the **Annales de Chimie** in 1789 and as published at that time, was issued in irregular series:-

Annales de Chimie. *

| | Series I | 1789-1815 | Vols. 1-96 |

Annales de Chimie et de Physique.

	Series II	1816-1840	Vols. 1-75
	Series III	1841-1863	Vols. 1-69
	Series IV	1864-1873	Vols. 1-30
	Series V	1874-1883	Vols. 1-30
	Series VI	1884-1893	Vols. 1-30
	Series VII	1894-1903	Vols. 1-30
	Series VIII	1904-1913	Vols. 1-30

Annales de Chimie. (A separate **Annales de Physique** was published from 1914).

	Series IX	1914-1923	Vols. 1-20
	Series X	1924-1933	Vols. 1-20
	Series XI	1934-1945	Vols. 1-20
	Series XII	1946-	Vols. 1-

Collective Indexes have been published for most of the later series.

The **Comptes rendus hebdomadaires des Séances de l'Académie des Sciences** are commonly regarded as starting in 1835, as the first volume covering chemical phenomena was issued in that year and is usually referred to as Vol. 1, previous publications or records of the French Academy being generally unavailable except by consultation of the **Procès-verbaux des Sciences de l'Academie depuis la Fondation** (*i.e.* from 1666-1835). In each subsequent year two volumes of the **Comptes**

* See Note 1, Appendix III.

Rendus have been published up to the present time. In general the papers in this journal serve merely to announce and describe in a general manner the results of investigations rather than to give details of the methods by which these advances have been brought about. A cumulative index for the 1835-1895 period is now available. The **Annales de Chimie** usually contains the most complete French original papers.

Chimie et Industrie began publication in 1918 and now issues two volumes per annum. It covers a field similar to that of **J. Appl. Chem.** The **Journal de Pharmacie et de Chimie** (originally known as **Bulletin de Pharmacie**) was first published in 1809. The following series were published:-

Series [1]	1809-1814*	1 Vol. per year
Series [2]	1815-1841*	1 Vol. per year
Series [3]	1842-1864	2 Vols. per year
Series [4]	1865-1879	2 Vols. per year
Series [5]	1880-1894	2 Vols. per year
Series [6]	1895-1909	2 Vols. per year
Series [7]	1910-1924	2 Vols. per year
Series [8]	1925-1939	2 Vols. per year
Series [9]	1940-1942†	

2·34. *German:* The **Annalen der Chemie** or **Liebig's Annalen** as it is often called, was founded by *Justus von Liebig* in 1832; for many years it was published at the rate of four volumes per year, each consisting of three numbers.

After 1872, it became somewhat irregular, several extra volumes appearing in certain years (e.g. eight between 1860 and 1872). This irregularity was largely due to extra matter submitted for publication; in recent years there has been an irregularity of another kind, namely, partial cessation of publication due to war conditions. The first volume of 1945 is numbered 557. The **Annalen** constitutes one of the most valuable repositories of research results, and ranks in importance next to the communications of the great national societies. Access to the **Annalen** is essential to chemical research. The **Annalen** is now exclusively devoted to organic chemistry, but

---

* Known as the **Bulletin de Pharmacie.**
† In this year, this journal became merged with the **Bulletin des Sciences Pharmacologiques** under the name **Annales Pharmaceutiques francaises.**

its articles are very comprehensive and usually contain valuable summaries of previous work. Cumulative indexes were published regularly up to Vol. 380.

Liebig's **Annalen** must not be confused with **Poggendorf's Annalen.** This **Annalen** series commenced in 1799 as **Gilbert's Annalen**, taking its name from the editor. The early volumes contained chemical matter, but the more recent issues are almost entirely devoted to physics, as is indicated by the present title; the various changes are:-

Gilbert's Annalen.
      Series I   1799 - 1824   Vols. 1-76
Poggendorf's Annalen.
      Series II   1824*- 1877   Vols. 1-160
Wiedemann's Annalen.
      Series III 1877*- 1899   Vols. 1-69
Annalen der Physik.
      Series IV   1900 - 1925   Vols. 1-50
      Series V   1926 -   Vols. 1-43/1943

* The break in series took place in the course of the year.

The **Journal für Praktische Chemie** was first published in 1834 and continued under this title until Vol. 162 of May, 1943, During the main part of its life it published original communications in many branches of chemical endeavour and was in many respects similar to the **Annalen** and **Berichte.** It is now continued as the **Journal für Makromolekular Chemie.** Cumulative indexes were published in 1843, 1853, 1863, 1869, 1894 and 1920.

Monatshefte für Chemie und verwandte Teile anderer Wissenschaften was first published in 1880 from Vienna, and has regularly issued an annual volume. It contains much of the communications of Austrian research workers, and was, during its early history, met with (differently paginated) as **Sitzungsberichte der kaiserlichen Akademie der Wissenschaft in Wien,** a publication which resembled in many ways our **Transactions of the Royal Society.**

German scientists were among the first to found special publications for restricted fields of chemical research; the term **Zeitschrift** corresponds to 'periodical' (**Berichte** means 'report'), and various periodicals were started as set out below:-

Zeitschrift für Analytische Chemie, (Z. Anal. Chem.) (1862)* Has surveyed analytical chemistry regularly since 1862, until 1944-5, which years were irregular.

Zeitschrift für angewandte Chemie, (1888). (Now called, since 1932, **Angewandte Chemie**), (**Z. Angew. Chem.**). In 1932 the name was changed, as indicated, but in 1942 a further change to **Die Chemie** was made, but was rescinded in 1947. When first issued this journal (mainly of technological interest) was in three parts:-

      i. General.
     ii. Abstracts.
    iii. Commercial.

The latter portion has now become merged in **Die Chemische Industrie** but the two other parts persist as **Teil A. Wissenschaftliche Teil** (scientific part); and **Teil B. Technisch-Wirtschaftlicher Teil** (Commercial part; literally 'technical economics').

Zeitschrift für anorganische Chemie, (1892). (From 1915 to 1943, Vols. 92-252, entitled **Zeit. f. anorg. und Allgemeine Chemie**), (**Z. Anorg. Chem.**). As its title implies, this journal is restricted to inorganic chemistry. Cumulative indexes for Vols. 1-50, 51-100, 101-150 are published.

Kolloid Zeitschrift, until 1913 (Vol. 12) was called by the title **Zeitschrift für Chemie und Industrie der Kolloide.** It is a journal for all aspects of colloid chemistry.

Zeitschrift für Electrochemie und angewandte physikalische Chemie, (1894), (**Z. Electrochem.**), deals chiefly with electrochemistry, but often has accounts of work in other spheres of physical chemistry.

Zeitschrift für Kristallographie, Mineralogie und Petrographie, (1877), (**Z. Krist. Min. Pet.**) began publication as the **Zeitschrift für Kristallographie und Mineralogie** in 1877 and continued as such until 1915 (Vol. 55), when a temporary cessation of publication was followed by completion of Vol. 55 in 1920, and a change of title (1921) to **Zeitschrift für Kristallographie** (or Part A of

* Indicates the date of publication of Vol. 1.

the whole work), and **Mineralogische und petrographische Mitteilungen** (being Part B). It deals with all phases of crystallography, crystal-geometry, crystal-physics and crystal-chemistry and their applications. The first 50 vols. have a cumulative index.

Zeitschrift für Untersuchung der Lebensmittel, (1870), (Z. Unt. Lebensm.), began publication as **Z. für Untersuchung der Nahrungs- und Genuss-mittel** but changed to the present title in 1921 (Vol. 51). Devoted to food research, this journal apparently ceased publication in 1943 (Vol. 85), and combined with **Vorratspflege und Lebensmittel-Untersuchung und Forschung** (Vol. 86, 1943).

Zeitschrift für physikalische Chemie, (1887), (Z. Physik. Chem.) was published regularly until 1916, when a marked slowing down is observed (Vol. 92, the second volume of 1916, covers 1917 and 1918 as well.) This journal was divided into two parts in 1929: **Abt. A. Chemische Thermodynamik, Kinetik, Electrochemie und Eigenschaftlehre; Abt. B. Chemie der Elementarprozesse Aufbau der Materie** but these were recombined from July, 1943. The journal is an extremely valuable one dealing with many aspects of physical chemistry in detail. Two cumulative indexes cover the period up to 1905.

Zeitschrift für physiologische Chemie (Hoppe-Seyler's), (1877), (Z. Physiol. Chem.), as its name implies deals with physiological chemical studies. It is occasionally referred to in older books of reference as **Hoppe-Seyler's Zeitschrift.**

2·35. **University Journals.** Many universities, especially in the U.S.A., publish chemical journals of their own. Much of the material published therein appears again in the national chemical journals, but there is a small residue which for different reasons remains unpublished. Again, the full details of doctoral theses, deposited in university libraries are not always available in published work, although much of the contents of such theses ultimately finds its way to general publication. ASLIB has done a great service in publishing an **Index to Theses accepted for higher degrees in the Universities of Great Britain and Ireland**, Vol. 1, 1950-1951; Vol. 2, 1951-1952. The publication is being continued. Examples from this country of university chemical journals would include the **Transactions** and reprints of the **Alembic Club** and the **Scientific Journal of the Royal College of Science** which contains as an integral part the **Journal of the Imperial College Chemical Society.**

Some notes on earlier Chemical Journals.

2·36. **Annalen** and **Annales.**

Annalen unaccompanied by any other designation, or contracted to **Ann.** is a reference to the **Annalen** of *Liebig*; as also is **Ann. Chem. Pharm.** The latter is a reference to the fact that the short-lived **Annalen der Pharmacie** (1832-1839) was merged with the **Annalen der Chemie.**

Ann. Chim. is a reference to **Annales de Chimie** and must bear a date prior to 1816 or after 1913 as between these dates (inclusive) the **Annales de Chimie** and the **Annales de Physique** were combined and any reference would be to **Ann. Chim. Phys.**

The earlier series of the **Annalen der Physik** are quite often cited as **Pogg. Ann.** or **Gilb. Ann.** There was a publication known as **Crell's Annalen** extant between 1784 and 1804. Its full title was **Chemische Annalen für die Freunde der Naturlehre, von L. Crell.**

2·37. **Some Obsolete Journals.**

Dingler's Polytechnisches Journal began publication in 1829 and continued until 1914 when it ceased with Vol. 329. After World War I it was revived but again ceased in 1931 (Vol. 346). The **Moniteur Scientifique**, a discursive publication, commenced in 1857 and continued through various series until 1926.

The **Atti della reale Accademia Lincei** commenced publication in 1851, and although not strictly obsolete its vicissitudes may be considered here. Its title at the original issue was, until 1869, **Atti dell'Accademia Pontificia dei nuovi Lincei,** and its volume numbers during this period were irregular; it continued until 1943 when publication ceased with Series [7] Vol. 5, Nos. 1-4. The name had been changed in 1921 to **Atti della reale Accademia nazionale dei Lincei.** The *Reale Accademia d'Italia* was suppressed and the journals ceased. A new journal under a similar title commenced publication in Jan., 1946.

The **Chemical News** was first published in 1859 and continued regularly until Oct. 1932 when, with Vol. 145, No. 3781, it ceased. It was originally a journal for the rapid publication of scientific results and was originally entitled **The Chemical News and Journal of Physical Science**, this name being changed in 1921 to **The Chemical News and Journal of Industrial Science.** There is much interesting and unique matter in the earlier volumes. In 1938 the **Chemical News** was revived under the title **Chemical Products and The Chemical News** and has since been published monthly, but the character of the journal little resembles that of the original publication.

The **Sitzungsberichte der Akademie der Wissenschaften in Wien, Abt.** IIB **(Chemie)** was a journal containing many chemical papers; it became somewhat irregular in appearance during 1943; in 1947 the title was changed to **Österreichische Akademie der Wissenschaften.** The same original subdivisions are made, so that Section IIB is for chemical communications. Some of the papers also appeared in the **Monatshefte für Chemie,** the correspondence between these two journals is given in the special Table on pages 141-2.

The **Revue générale de chimie pure et appliquée** ran for twenty-one years but was discontinued in 1918. It dealt mainly with reviews of industrial procedures and semi-technical subjects.

An **Appendix** will be found at the end of this book in which the less common obsolete journals are listed.

2·4. **Ancillary and Technical Journals.** There are thousands of journals devoted to chemical technology, and it would be impossible to list them all in a work of this nature. The abstracting bureaux publish from time to time a comprehensive list of the journals from which their abstracts are prepared; perhaps the most comprehensive is that published by **Chemical Abstracts** 1956, (A.C.S. Special Publication; 314 pp.). This may be purchased separately. Nearly every aspect of chemical science has its appropriate journals in which the topics peculiar to the subject are discussed, and, in addition, the borderland subjects have their own periodicals, often, as in the case of biochemistry and pharmacology, as complex and erudite as those of chemistry itself.

Some journals of applied science (or borderland science) are of high value and are classed as 'permanent'; others are mainly concerned with slight reviews of day-to-day interest and are often termed 'ephemeral', their value and importance decreasing with time. It has been thought best to give examples of all kinds and to subdivide them according to the subjects treated. It is possible that the publication of some of the German journals mentioned below may have ceased.

2·41. **Documentation.** The study of chemical literature is, in itself a subject for publication, dealing with how and where chemical imformation is compiled, stored and used. Papers on such matters are often to be found in **Aslib* Proceedings (GB)**†, the **Journal of Documentation (GB)**, **American Documentation (US)** and the **Journal of Chemical Education (US)**. For books, there is a **Technical Book Review Index (US)** which commenced about 1916 and was discontinued during the period 1928-1935, but is running again now. Documentation and problems in the history of chemical discoveries are to be met with also in **Isis (US)**, an international review devoted to the history of science and civilization, in **Annals of Science (GB)** and also in **Documentation Scientifique (F)**, and **Information (US)**.

The following of patent citations and specifications is an important branch of documentation and, apart from the printed specifications themselves, much information can be obtained by consulting **The Official Gazette of the U.S. Patent Office**, the **Official Journal** (of British Patents) and the **Octroiraad Nederland.**

2·42. There is no journal devoted exclusively to the apparatus of the chemical laboratory, but the **Journal of Scientific Instruments (GB)** and **Instruments (US)** with **Z. Instrumentkunde (G)** deal with many of the more physical of the instruments used in chemical work. There are also many journals in which

---

* Aslib – the **Association of Special Libraries and Information Bureaux** – is a valuable organization which serves to coordinate the work of the bodies cited in its title; it also acts in an advisory capacity. A somewhat similar organization in the U.S.A. is the **Special Libraries Association of New York.**

† To avoid unnecessary repetition, initials will be used to indicate the country of origin: **(GB)**, Great Britain; **(US)**, United States; **(F)**, France; **(S)**, Switzerland; **(SW)**, Sweden; **(G)**, Germany; **(I)**, Italy; **(USSR)**, Russia.

spectrographic communications are presented, some like **Spectrochimica Acta** (G) being specifically devoted to this subject.

The technique of microscopy, on which so much scientific progress is based, is well provided with journals such as:-

1. Journal of the Royal Microscopical Society (GB).
2. Journal of the Quekett Microscopical Club (GB).
3. The Microscope and Entomological Monthly (GB).
4. The Quarterly Journal of Microscopical Science (GB).
5. Stain Technology (US).
6. Transactions of the American Microscopical Society.
7. Zeitschrift für wissenschaftliche Mikroscopie (G).

2·43. Sub-atomic and radioactive phenomena. Much data on this subject is scattered through the standard journals on physics, which cannot, of course, be catalogued here. The **Physikalische Zeitschrift** (G) has a special section on radioactivity and the same subject is dealt with in **Travaux de l'institut d'état de radium** (USSR). **Electronics** (US) also has articles on this subject. **Nuclear Physics** (US) was started in 1955 and **Nucleonics** (US) in 1947.

2·44. Electrochemistry, and its industrial applications, is covered by a large number of journals, many of them ephemeral in nature. More weighty are the **Z. Electrochem.** already mentioned (on page 19), **Transactions of the Electrochemical Society** (US) and a number of highly specialized trade journals such as the **Journal of the Electrodepositors Technical Society** (GB).

2·45. Photographic chemical **technology** is to be found recorded in the **Photographic Journal** (GB) and in **Photographic Abstracts** (GB) published by the *Royal Photographic Society;* in **Photographische Industrie** (G) and in **Zeitschrift für wissenschaftliche Photographie und Photochemie** (G); whilst the **Fotokhimicheskaya Promyshlennost** (USSR) shews that at least one journal is devoted to the photochemical industry.

2·46. News. The news and views of scientists give rise to a whole series of journals; some like **Nature** (GB), and **The New Scientist** (GB), deal also with other sciences, **Science** (US) and **Current Science (India),** are media in which new discoveries are announced, usually by a short letter, pending the slower publication of full details elsewhere. **Nature** has an extensive series of book reviews, and an index of new books published, which is a valuable feature; in addition, one can always rely on there being an authoritative summary of any outstanding scientific advance, whether chemical or otherwise, in **Nature** at an early date. These features, together with news of scientific affairs, make **Nature** a 'must' in the reading of any chemist. Not being confined solely to chemical topics, it is invaluable for giving the chemist some appreciation of what is going on in fields other than his own.

Other papers in which both news and review articles of importance are published include **Chemistry and Industry (GB)** an official publication of the *Society of Chemical Industry;* **Chemical and Engineering News (US)** officially published by the *American Chemical Society;* **Experientia (S);** **Umschau (G);** **Teknisk Tidskrift (SW);** **The Industrial** Chemist (GB); **Science News Letter (US);** **Discovery (GB);** **Tidskrift für Kjemi Bergvessen og Metallurgi (Norway);** **Endeavour (GB);** **Research (GB);** **Science Progress (GB);** **Scientia (I);** **Revue Scientifique (F);** **Naturwissenschaften (G);** and such publications as the **Scientific Monthly** issued by the *American Association for the Advancement of Science* and **The Advancement of Science** issued by the *British Association for the Advancement of Science.* All these together with such papers as **The Chemical Age,** and the **Chemical Trade Journal,** provide a forum for the exchange of news and the discussion of views on current affairs of chemistry.

2.47. Analytical Chemistry. The Analyst (GB) and **Analytical Chemistry (US)** are probably the two most important journals in this field. The former is in its eightieth year and is the official organ of the *Society for Analytical Chemistry,* until recently known as the *Society of Public Analysts and other Analytical Chemists;* there are decennial indexes to **The Analyst** covering the decennia ending 1905, 1915, 1925, 1935 1945 & 1955. **Analytical Chemistry** is an official publication of the *American Chemical Society,* and was originally issued in 1931 as part of the **J. Ind. Eng. Chem.** but since 1947 it has been issued separately. Other analytical publications are **The Journal of the Association of Official Agricultural Chemists (US), Zeitschrift für Analytische Chemie (G)** and **Mikrochimica**

Acta (G) now (since 1938) united with **Mikrochemie.**

The **Chemist-Analyst,** a useful publication of laboratory methods and devices, has been somewhat irregular in appearance. The table below gives its bibliographical record:-

Year	Numbers	Year	Volume	Numbers
1911	1- 3	1927	16	2 (Oct.)
1912	4- 6	1928	17	1-4
1913	7	1929	18	1-6
1914	8-11	(1911-1929)	Subject-Author Index	
1915	12-15	1930	19	1-5
1916	16-19	1931	20	1-6
1917	20-23	1932	21	1-6
1918	24-27	1933	22	1-4
1919	28-29	1934	23	1-4
1920	30-31	1935	24	1-4
1921	32-35	1936	25	1-4
1922	36-38	1937	26	1-4
1923	39-40	1938	27	1-3
1924	41-42	1939	28	1-3
1925	43-45	1940	29	1-4
1926	46-48	1941	30	1-4
1927	49 (Feb.-Mar.)	1942	31	1-4
		1943	32	1-4
		1944	33	1-4
		1945	34	1-4
		1946	35	1-4
		1947	36	1-3
		1948	37	1-4
		1949	38	1-4
		1951	39	1-4
		1950	40	1-4

2·48. Mineralogical and Geological Chemistry. There are many journals devoted exclusively to geology and mineralogy, which have occasional papers of chemical interest. Of these, the following may be cited as examples:-

1. **The Quarterly Journal of the Geological Society of London** (GB).
2. **Zeitschrift fur Kristallographie, Mineralogie und Petrographie** (G); of this, the A section is of most

chemical interest.

3. **Zentrallblatt für Mineralogie, Geologie und Paläontologie (G).**
4. **Zhurnal Geofisiki (USSR).**
5. **Transactions of the American Geophysical Society.**
6. **Rock Products (US).**
7. **Rocks and Minerals (US).**
8. **Geochimica et Cosmochimica Acta (GB).**

2·49. **Metallurgy and Metallography.** There is a vast literature of this subject, as might be expected from the part played by metals in world economics. A broad division is made, as a general rule, between ferrous and non-ferrous metallurgy, and journals dealing with the former seldom accept communications on the latter section. Thus, we have in the ferrous division, **The Journal of the Iron and Steel Institute (GB)**, **Steel (US)**, **Stahl und Eisen (G)**, in which scientific communications are to be found; there are in the non-ferrous section, **The Journal of the Institute of Metals (GB)**, and **Metallurgical Abstracts**, together with such trade papers as **The Light Metal Age (US)**, **Iron Age**, and general metallurgical publications such as **The Transactions of the American Institute of Mining and Metallurgical Engineers (US)**, **Revue de Metallurgie (F)**, **Mining and Metallurgy (US)** and **The Metal Industry (US)**.

2·50. **Biological Chemistry.** Mention has already been made (page 20) of the **Zeitschrift für Physiologische Chemie (Hoppe-Seyler)**; to this may be added the two main biochemical journals, namely **The Biochemical Journal (GB)** which commenced publication in 1906 and the **Journal of Biological Chemistry (US)**. Much biochemical data is given in journals (e.g. **The Journal of Nutrition, Phytochemical Journal**) primarily devoted to other aspects of the subject.

2·51. **Foods.** It is only natural that the important subject of food chemistry should be well documented. Scientific communications are made to such journals as **The Journal of Nutrition (US)**, **The Journal of Milk Technology (US)**, **Journal of the Institute of Brewing (GB)**, and the **Journal of Dairy Research (GB)**, whilst numerous abstracts and reviews are published, e.g. **Nutrition Abstracts and Reviews (US)**, **Dairy Science Abstracts (GB)**. The following examples are typical of the general and specialized papers dealing with current foodstuffs topics; Food Industries (US), Food Manufacture (GB), Food Research (US), Food (GB), Flavours (GB), Tea Quarterly (Ceylon), The Tea and Coffee Trades Journal (US), Western Canner and Packer (US).

2·52. Chemical Engineering. The Transactions of the Institution of Chemical Engineers (GB) and the Transactions of the American Institute of Chemical Engineers (US) are the official organs of the professional chemical engineers in Great Britain and the United States. In addition, much chemical engineering data is published in Industrial and Engineering Chemistry (US), in the Proceedings of the Chemical Engineering Group of the Society of Chemical Industry (GB) and Chemical Engineering Progress (GB). There are also such journals as Chemical Engineering (US) and the Industrial Chemist (GB) which deal with the more industrial aspects of the subject.

2·53. Water, Sewage and Sanitation. Pure water and efficient sewage disposal are aspects of modern civilization and are largely the responsibility of specialized chemists. Among journals devoted to these fields will be found:-

1. Water and Sewage Works (US).
2. Water (Dutch).
3. Sewage Works and Municipal Sanitation (US).
4. Archives of Industrial Hygiene and Occupational Medicine (US), formerly (until 1950) Journal of Industrial Hygiene and Toxicology.

2·54. Agriculture. The field of agricultural chemistry is well provided with journals, including the newly founded Journal of the Science of Food and Agriculture (see page 15) whilst many deal with the study of soil, as Soil Research (G), Journal of Soil Science (GB) and Soil Science (US), while yet others deal with the borderland subjects relating to agriculture, for example, Phytopathology (US), Plant Physiology (US) and the Journal of Agricultural Science (GB). There is, of course, a similar series of journals dealing with veterinary science, the Veterinary Journal (GB), The Veterinary Record (GB) and Veterinary Medicine (US), in which communications of interest to the chemist are sometimes encountered.

2·55. Fermentation. Originally concerned almost solely with brewing, vinification and vinegar manufacture, older journals such as **Wines and Vines** (US), the **Journal of the Institute of Brewing** (GB) are still largely concerned with these subjects. The recognition of the life-forms responsible for these arts has led to the establishment of the whole science of microbiology which stands as a link between chemical and medical science. Such publications as the **Journal of Bacteriology** (US), **Proceedings of the Society of Applied Bacteriology** (GB), **Microbiology** (USSR), **Bacteriological Reviews** (US) and the **Review of Applied Mycology** (GB) are but a few of those entirely devoted to this division of science.

2·56. **Medical Chemistry.** The literature of medicine is as voluminous as – probably more voluminous than – the literature of chemistry. Every division of medicine and surgery, and many subdivisions, has its own journal, and abstracting bureaux search them for the occasional chemically interesting communication. Inasmuch as life is a continual manifestation of chemical change, it is not surprising that certain of these journals have a more chemical trend than others. The following examples indicate types of journals to be searched in connexion with studies of compounds exhibiting physiological action:-

1. **Journal of Physiology** (US).
2. **Journal of Pathology and Bacteriology** (GB).
3. **Vitamine und Hormone** (G).
4. **Proceedings of the Society for Experimental Biology and Medicine** (US).
5. **Journal of Pharmacology and Experimental Therapeutics** (US).
6. **Archiv für experimentelle Pathologie und Pharmakologie** (G).
7. **Helvetica Physiologica Acta** (S).
8. **Helvetica Pharmacologica Acta** (S).
9. **Journal of Experimental Medicine** (US).

2·57. **Pharmaceutical Chemistry.** Most of the journals of pharmacy are the ephemeral type; exceptions, however, are such publications as the **Quarterly Journal of Pharmacy and Pharmacology** (GB), the **Pharmaceutical Journal** (GB) and the **Journal of the American Pharmaceutical Association.** Applied pharmacy and the news angle are catered for by a wealth of journals such as the **Chemist and Druggist** (GB) and the **Manufacturing Chemist** (GB).

2·58. **Perfumery Science.** This highly specialized corner of applied chemistry is amply provided with trade journals such as the **Perfumery and Essential Oil Record** (GB), **Parfumerie Moderne** (F), **Industrie de la Parfumerie** (F) and **Riechstoffe Industrie und Kosmetik** (G).

2·59. **Ceramics and Glass.** These, being important applications of chemical science, have a wealth of specialized journals, among which are numbered the **Transactions of the British Ceramic Society** (GB), **The Journal of the American Ceramic Association** (US), **Glass** (GB), **Ceramic Industry** (US), **Journal of the Society of Glass Technology** (GB), **The Refractories Journal** (GB), **The Glass Research Association Bulletins** (GB) and many Continental and Asiatic journals such as **Verre et Silicates Industriels** (Belg.), and **Zpravy Csekoslovenske Keramicke Spolecnosti** (Czk.).

2·60. **Building and Road Materials.** Examples of journals devoted to this branch are **Road Abstracts** (GB), **Roads and Streets** (US), **Revue des materiaux de construction et de travaux publiques** (F) and **Public Roads** (US).

2·61. **Fuels and Carbonizable Products.** The **Journal of the Institute of Fuel** (GB) is an example of the more scientific of such papers, and among the more technological are the **Oil and Gas Journal** (US), **Oel und Kohle** (G), **Fuel** (GB), and the **Gas Age** (US).

2·62. **Petroleum and its Products.** There are nearly a hundred publications of various types devoted to the science and industry of petroleum; some examples are the **Journal of the Institute of Petroleum** (GB), **World Petroleum** (US), **Petroleum Processing** (US), **Petroleum Technology** (US), **Petroleum World** (US), **Petroleum Refining** (US). Examples of publications devoted to products allied to petroleum are **Lubrication** (US) and **Teer und Bitumen** (G).

2·63. **Cellulose and Paper.** Much of the literature of this subject is concerned with the mechanical process of paper and board making and is not of a specifically chemical nature. However, as the process is fundamentally a chemical one, chemical discussions are found in such papers as the **Paper Trade Journal** (US), **Zeitschrift für Papier, Pappe, Zellulose** und Holzstoff (G), Wood Products (US) and The Pulp and Paper Industry (US).

2·64. **Explosives.** There is probably less published work in this field, in relation to the amount of research done, than in others. Some is published in the physical-chemical journals, but such publications as the **Explosives Engineer** (US) deal primarily with the applications of explosives and not with their manufacture and chemistry. There is also much useful information in Z. Schiess u. Sprengstoffwesen.

2·65. **Dyes and Textiles.** Here again, many publications deal with the mechanics of dyeing, bleaching and textile manipulations, e.g. **Journal of the Textile Institute** (GB), **Zellwolle** (G), **Wool Record and Textile World** (GB), **Textile Age** (US), **Textile Mercury and Argus** (GB), **American Dyestuffs Reporter** (US), **Textile Research Journal** (US), **Melliand's Textilberichte** (G), and the many **Rayon** journals. On the other hand, the dyestuffs themselves may be found discussed in the **Journal of the Society of Dyers and Colourists** (GB).

2·66. **Paints, Varnishes and Lacquers.** The literature is almost entirely taken up with the technology of the field, as in the **Paint, Oil and Chemical Review** (US), **Oil and Colour Trades Journal** (GB), **National Paint Bulletin** (US), **Paint Technology** (GB) and **Journal of the Oil and Colour Chemists Association.**

2·67. **Fats, Fatty Oils, Waxes and Detergents.** This section, and the four sections (2·68-2·71) which follow, are similar in that they all have journals dealing with their own peculiar technology which are seldom encountered by chemists in other fields. It is, therefore, proposed to give only a few indicative examples of each:-

1. **Soap, Perfumery and Cosmetics** (GB).
2. **Soap and Sanitary Chemicals** (US).
3. **Seifensieder Zeitung** (G).
4. **Fette und Seifen** (G).
5. **Journal of the American Oil Chemists Society.**
   (formerly **Oil and Soap**).

2·68. **Sugar, Starch and Gums.** A highly technical field in which 'know-how' is more often sought after than fundamental scientific data. Examples of its journals are:-

1. Sugar (GB).
2. Sucrerie Belge (*Belgium*).
3. Zuckerindustrie (G).

2·69. **Leather and Glue.** A highly developed facet of industrial chemistry in which a high degree of scientific control is involved. Examples of its special literature are:-

1. The Leather Trades Review (GB).
2. The Leather World (has a monthly scientific section) (GB).
3. Journal of the International Society of Leather Trades Chemists (GB).
4. Journal of the American Leather Chemists Association (US).

2·70. **Rubber and other Elastomers.** It is rarely that we encounter papers dealing with the structure and chemical properties of rubber in the technical press; these are more often published in the usual scientific journals. The four papers mentioned below are concerned with the technology of rubber and of its synthetic substitutes:-

1. Transactions of the Institution of the Rubber Industry (GB).
2. Rubber Chemistry and Technology (US).
3. The Rubber Age (US).
4. The Rubber Age and Synthetics (GB).
5. Rubber (*Holland*).
6. India Rubber Journal (GB).

2·71. **Synthetic Resins and Plastics.** The sudden rise to prominence of plastics during the last three decades has been accompanied by a parallel rise in specialized literature. Besides the two journals cited as examples below there is a whole host of ephemeral publications dealing with the superficial aspects of the plastics industry:-

1. The Journal of Polymer Science (US). This is a valuable scientific journal, and appears somewhat irregularly. The years and volume numbers are:-

1946	1947	1948	1949	1950	1951	1952	1953	1954	1955
1	2	3	4	5	6,7	8,9	10,11	12,*13,14	

* Symposium on macromolecules held by IUPAC in Uppsala.

2. Modern Plastics (US).
3. Plastics (GB).
4. British Plastics (GB).
5. Kuntstoffe (G).

2.72. **General.** Two very valuable series of what may be regarded as specialized monographs are published (a) by *The Chemical Society* and (b) by the *American Chemical Society*. The former are known as 'special publications' and comprise volumes on:-

(1) **The Kinetics and Mechanism of Inorganic Reactions in Solution.**
(2) **Symposium on Peptide Chemistry.**
(3) **Recent work on Naturally Occurring Nitrogen Heterocyclic Compounds.**

The second are entitled '**Advances in Chemistry Series**' and fifteen volumes have appeared:-

1. Agricultural Control Chemicals.
2. Chemical Factors in Hypertension.
3. Analytical Methods in the Food Industry.
4. Searching the Chemical Literature.
5. Progress in Petroleum Technology.
6. Azeotropic Data.
7. Agricultural Applications of Petroleum Products.
8. Chemical Nomenclature.
9. Fire Retardant Paints.
10. Literature Resources for Chemical Process Industries.
11. Natural Plant Hydrocolloids.
12. Uses of Sugars and other Carbohydrates in the Food Industry.
13. Pesticides in Tropical Agriculture.
14. Nomenclature for Terpene Hydrocarbons.
15. Physical Properties of Chemical Compounds.

These volumes are mostly the records of symposia and constitute authoritative summaries in the fields.

CHAPTER III

ABSTRACT JOURNALS

THE great volume of original communications made in the journals described in the preceding chapters is such that no one person can read and become familiar with the whole. Systems of abstracts have, therefore, been devised to summarize the material, and to give an indication of the contents of the original papers, together with numerical data in a highly compressed form.

It is through these valuable publications that chemists keep in touch with the progress of their science. The principal journals of this character are:-

3·1. **British Abstracts.** The production of this abstracting service and journal was financed by several British scientific societies. Originally, in 1849, the *Chemical Society* commenced to publish its own abstracts, and was followed by the *Society of Chemical Industry* in 1882. It was found after a lapse of some years that an overlap existed in the work of these two abstracting bodies and in 1926 their activities were merged in a *Bureau* producing, in uniform format, **Abstracts A** (Pure Chemistry) and **Abstracts B** (Applied Chemistry), the joint title being **British Chemical Abstracts.** In 1937 the **A Abstracts** were split into three sections:-

Ai Pure Chemistry (General, Physical and Inorganic).
Aii Pure Chemistry (Organic Chemistry).
Aiii Pure Chemistry (Biochemistry).

The B section remained undivided. The three A sections were, however, paginated independently. In 1938 the title was amended to **British Chemical and Physiological Abstracts** when an agreement was reached with the *Biochemical Society* and the *Physiological Society* to co-operate in the production of abstracts; this marked, in effect, the amalgamation of **British Chemical Abstracts** and **Physiological Abstracts.** In 1939 a similar agreement with the *Anatomical Society of Great Britain and Ireland* secured the inclusion of four sections on anatomy. In 1941 the B (Applied Chemistry) abstracts were subdivided into:-

Bi   **General and Inorganic Industrial Chemistry.**
Bii **Industrial Organic Chemistry.**
Biii **Agriculture, Foods, Sanitation, etc.**

All six sections were further subdivided into convenient fields of reference. A further main section C (Analysis and Apparatus) added in 1944, replaced the abstracts published in the **Analyst** (see page 25). In 1945, the name was altered to **British Abstracts.** There were two separate author and subject indexes covering the A and C, and B and C abstracts respectively.

Collective, decennial and quinquennial indexes to **British Abstracts** (or their predecessors) are available as follows:-

1. 1848-1872 Collective.
2. 1873-1882 Decennial.
3. 1883-1892 Decennial.
4. 1893-1902 Decennial.
5. 1903-1912 Decennial.
6. 1913-1922 Decennial.
7. 1923-1932 Decennial.
8. 1933-1937 Quinquennial.

Until 1946 no Formula Indexes to **British Abstracts** were issued; the first formula index, covering the A, B and C abstracts was issued in 1946. This journal ceased publication in 1953. Since this date the following chemical abstracts have been published in Great Britain:-

(i) **Analytical Abstracts.** Commenced in 1954, a reversion to the abstracts published by the *Society for Analytical Chemistry* until 1944.

(ii) **The Journal of Applied Chemistry** commenced the publication of abstracts in applied chemistry in 1954. The abstracts resemble those of the previous **British Abstracts** in many respects.

(iii) **British Abstracts of Medical Science** has been recently (1955) started to fill gaps and extend coverage on a very wide field of biochemical and medical topics.

(iv) *The Chemical Society* publishes **Current Chemical Papers**, being a classified world list of titles of new papers in pure chemistry. This service began in 1954 and enables the chemist to see the titles of published research work more quickly than by waiting until the abstracts appear.

3·2. Chemical Abstracts. This series of abstracts began publication in 1907 and has been issued fortnightly since. It is a publication of the *American Chemical Society* and although divided into thirty-one parts, these are issued bound together and paginated serially. The two December issues are the indexes; the author index is usually issued in the March or April of the following year and the Subject Index about two months later. Author, Subject, Formula and Patent Indexes are published, and the following collective indexes of authors and subjects are available:-

1. 1907-1916.
2. 1917-1926.
3. 1927-1936.
4. 1937-1946.

A Collective formula index (1920-1946) was published in 1951, and it is the intention to publish Decennial (or other Collective) formula indexes with the corresponding Subject and Author Indexes, issue of the 1947-1956 Collective Index has started.

A full list of the 5236 periodicals from which **Chemical Abstracts** is compiled is given in a special publication (1956), (Suppt. 1958). A predecessor of **Chemical Abstracts**, called the **Review of American Chemical Research** was issued from 1895-1906, but it is now seldom consulted.

3·3. Chemisches Zentralblatt. In 1830, and until 1850, the **Pharmaceutisches Centralblatt** was published, and in the latter year became the **Chemisches und Pharmaceutisches Central-blatt.** After six years the name was shortened to **Chemisches Centralblatt,** and in 1897, with a change of C to Z, the 5th series was commenced and continued until the middle period of World War II when publication ceased in 1945 for a period and was then resumed on a limited scale in 1947; a so-called **Chemisches Zentralblatt** was published from two of the occupation zones, but both were merged in 1950. The present **Chem. Zent.** is now very similar to its prewar form, and the intervening gap (1945-1947) has been covered retrospectively in the recent years.

The two great abstract journals differ slightly in the treatment of the individual abstract and the method used for assembling them into book form. **Chemisches Zentralblatt** makes a broad division into pure and technical chemistry, while **Chemical Abstracts** gives slightly more detail as to the quantitative aspects of preparative work. There is little doubt that the latter publication has the most detailed and effective index while the formula indexes of the German and American works are very valuable publications to the organic chemist. The coverage differs slightly according to the policy of the two editorial bodies, but it is safe to say that no chemical paper of any importance is likely to be overlooked by either of them. The student is recommended to make himself familiar with both; it is sometimes necessary to use both in a search (e.g. in patent litigation) where it is essential that nothing be missed; in the majority of cases the worker usually settles down to use one or other of the systems according to his tastes.

3·4. **Japanese Chemical Abstracts** was founded in 1927 and from that date to 1938 seven volumes were published which covered the Japanese chemical literature from 1877-1926. From 1927 to July, 1945 the journal appeared monthly. Thence until 1951 publication was sparse and spasmodic but from 1951 to date normal publication has taken place.

3·5. **Biological Abstracts.** Started in 1926 and continued to date; valuable for biochemical data.

3·6. **Russian Abstracts.** Commencing in 1953 a Soviet chemical abstract series has appeared – **Referativnyi Zhurnal, Khimiya,** abbreviated to **RZhKhim.** The whole is in Russian and is published twice a month; it covers about 175-200,000 abstracts annually.

3·7. There are other abstracts, of a more highly specialized character, published by various specialist societies or organizations.   Included among such are:-

3.71. **The Patent Office Abridgements.** This journal
was first published in 1855, and there is a 50-year
index 1860-1910.

3.72. **Metallurgical Abstracts (General and non-ferrous)**
published by the *Institute of Metals*, and the
Abstracts of Current Literature published by the
Iron and Steel Institute are two of the leading
metallurgical abstracts series.

3.73. **The Abstracts of the Institute of Petroleum**
dealing exclusively with matters of interest to
petroleum covers engineering subjects such as
well-drilling as well as chemical matters.

3.74. **The Abstracts of the Society of Dyers and Colourists** has a scope which is sufficiently indicated
by its title.

3.75. **Review of current literature relating ro the Paint,
Colour, Varnish and Allied Industries.** In this
publication are abstracted and reviewed papers on
topics related to the subjects of the title.

3.76. **Fats, Oils and Detergents.** A loose-leaf abstract
service, issued monthly by *B. F. Daubert* and
covering about 800 pages per annum.   The series
started in 1947.

3.77. **Nuclear Science Abstracts.** This has been
issued twice monthly since 1947 by the *Atomic
Energy Commission.* A cumulative index to the
first four volumes is available.

3.8. Various fields of applied science (of a chemical nature)
are covered by the D.S.I.R. abstract publications.   They are:-

3.81. **Building Science Abstracts** is prepared by the
Building Research Station. It is published
monthly, and contains about 1800 abstracts annually, classified under the following headings:-

    Stone
    Clay and clay ware
    Glass
    Lime and plaster

Cement and concrete
Metals
Timber and cellulosic fibre building materials
Paint and varnish
Miscellaneous building materials
Plastics
Physics and chemistry
Testing and research methods
Soil mechanics and foundations
Theory and performance of structures
Building construction
Housing and planning
Fire resistance and grading
Plumbing and drainage
Heating and thermal insulation
Lighting
Ventilation and air conditioning
Acoustics and sound insulation
Specialized construction.

3·82. **Food Science Abstracts** is prepared by the *Food Investigation Organization*. It is published every two months. The publication contains about 1800 abstracts annually, covering the storage, preservation, transport and processing of food and classified under the following headings:-

Meat, including pig-flesh
Poultry and game
Fish and shell-fish
Eggs
Dairy produce
Fats and oils
Fruit and vegetables
Grains, crops and seed, animal feeding-stuffs
   and fodder
Processes
Packing methods and materials
Engineering.

3·83. **Fuel Abstracts** is prepared by the *Fuel Research Station*. It is published monthly. Collective subject and author indexes are issued every six months at the completion of each volume. The publication contains about 11000 abstracts annually, classified under the following headings:-

Natural solid fuels: winning, sources and properties, preparation
Manufactured solid fuels and carbon products: properties
Carbonization
Gasification
Gaseous fuels: properties and treatment
By-products of carbonization and gasification
Natural liquid fuels and lubricants: sources, properties and treatments
Synthetic fuels, lubricants and other products
Electricity and electric power
Steam raising and steam engines
Other prime movers
Industrial furnaces, kilns, combustion
Domestic heating, cooking, lighting, etc.
Atmospheric pollution
Refractories
Fundamental science related to fuel technology
Analysis, testing, instruments

3·84. **Road Abstracts** is prepared by the *Road Research Laboratory* of D.S.I.R. and the *Ministry of Transport*. It is published monthly. The publication contains about 1000 abstracts annually, classified under the following headings:-

Finance and organization
Planning, lay-out and surface characteristics
Soil engineering and drainage
Soil stabilization and low-cost roads
Road stone and aggregates
Tar and bitumen (including surface dressing)
Concrete
Other materials and constructional details
Maintenance
Bridges and other structures

Traffic and road user characteristics
Traffic marking, signs and signals
Vehicle and street lighting
Safety and accidents
Plant, machinery and apparatus.

3.85. **Water Pollution Abstracts** is prepared by the *Water Pollution Research Laboratory*. It is published monthly. The publication contains about 1500 abstracts annually, classified under the following headings:-

Water supplies
Analysis and examination of water
Sewage
Trade waste waters
Pollution of natural waters.

There are also many medical and pharmaceutical abstract systems, few of which need engage the attention of the chemist. An exception must be made for:-

3.9. **Excerpta Medica.** This is an abstract system for the medical sciences, published from Amsterdam. The fifteen sections (set out below) are separate, and may be subscribed for separately. They are:-

1. **Anatomy, anthropology, embryology and histology.**
*2. **Physiology, biochemistry and pharmacology.**
*3. **Endocrinology.**
*4. **Medical microbiology and hygiene.**
*5. **General pathology and pathological anatomy.**
*6. **Internal medicine.**
7. **Pediatrics.**
8. **Neurology and psychiatry.**
9. **Surgery.**
10. **Obstetrics and gynæcology.**
11. **Oto-, rhino and laryngology.**
12. **Ophthalmology.**
13. **Dermatology.**
14. **Radiology.**
15. **Tuberculosis.**

* These sections are most likely to have material of interest to the chemist.

Not all these sections are of equal interest to the chemist, but the interpenetration of chemical and medical fields is so great that the chemist, especially the organic chemist, often needs to examine medical abstracts. **Abstracts of World Medicine** is a similar and equally valuable series.

CHAPTER IV

TEXTBOOKS AND SPECIAL WORKS
OF REFERENCE

THIS section is not an attempt to catalogue the textbooks, compendia and monographs of chemistry, but gives an indication of the more important and commonly encountered source-books. For convenience the subject is divided thus:-

4·1. Historical.

4·2. Analytical.

4·3. Inorganic and Physical.

4·4. Mineral and Metallurgical.

4·5. Biochemistry.

4·6. Organic Chemistry.

4·7. Annual Reviews.

4·8. Applied Chemistry.

4·9. Nuclear Chemistry.

Broadly speaking, the group may be divided into compendia, monographs and textbooks. A compendium such as **Beilstein** or **Gmelin** attempts to cover the whole of a wide field of chemical endeavour, and to range the information in order, rather like an enormous encyclopædia, except that the entries are not usually made alphabetically. This type of work is more particularly described in the section on 'Organic Chemistry' (4·6), and has the characteristic that it attempts to cover the whole range completely.

A monograph is devoted to a detailed (often, but not necessarily, complete) survey of a single topic, or portion of a topic. It is usually fully documented. There are series of such monographs published in most countries; that of the *American Chemical Society* (A.C.S. monographs) is perhaps the most extensive and contains about ninety volumes on very varied chemical topics. The completeness of monographs, in a bibliographical sense, has been much discussed. In some cases where the writer has carried out much research in a given field, and has read, over a long period of years, all that has been written on it, a monograph fully documented from primary sources is written; on the other hand, less experienced workers with some knowledge of the field, write useful monographs from secondary sources, such as abstracts. Although the latter type of monograph can be useful, its bibliographical limitations should be borne in mind. Further, the limitations which the author of a monograph has imposed on the scope of his work are often implied, rather than expressed. Thus, for example, a monograph on **Methylene Blue and Related Compounds** might discuss the subject wholly from the strictly chemical standpoint and entirely ignore the application of such dyestuffs in dyeing, milk-testing and bacteriology. In any case, in the absence of a specific assurance by the author, it is not safe to accept the documentation of a monograph as complete.

Textbooks are in no sense complete surveys; they seldom purport to be more than a selection of some more important aspects of a topic, and, even then, give only a sketch of the field. Nevertheless, the more serious textbooks often offer an excellent introduction to the literature and may be read with profit before commencing a detailed search. Examples of the more valuable compendia, monographs and textbooks are given in the following sections.

4·1. **Historical.**

E. F. Armstrong, **Chemistry in the Twentieth Century**, edited by *E. F. Armstrong* (1924). An account written by various authorities, primarily for the Wembley Exhibition chemical exhibits, describing the achievements and state of knowledge in chemical science of about a quarter of a century ago.

S. Arrhenius, **Theories of Chemistry**, edited by *T. S. Price* (1907). Founded on a series of lectures given by the author in America. This work gives a good picture of the development of chemical theory up to the turn of the century.

A. J. Berry, **Modern Chemistry: Some Sketches of its Historical Development** (1946). A useful book for the chemist who wants a quick perspective view of major developments in this field.

J. A. W. Bugge, **Das Buch der Grosser Chemiker** (1949), contains a mass of valuable historical references.

H. J. Pledge, **Science since 1500** (1939), a readable account of scientific (not exclusively chemical) development.

The Chemical Society, **Memorial Lectures**, [2 Vols. 1893-1900 (1901); 1901-1913 (1914) and thereafter throughout the **Journal**]. These are the memorial lectures to distinguished chemists given before the Society. They form a valuable historical commentary on the progress of chemical science, and apart from the matter they contain are well worth reading for the excellent style which usually characterizes them.

E. Cohen, **Jacobus Henricus van't Hoff, sein Leben u. Wirken** (1912). A full biography of one of the pioneers of modern physical chemistry, and valuable for its general account of contemporary chemical science.

W. C. Dampier, **A Shorter History of Science** (1944). Excellent for obtaining a picture of chemistry in relation to the other sciences.

A. Findlay, **A Hundred Years of Chemistry** (1937). A valuable survey, giving a good and well-balanced account of the progress during the period.

I. Freund, **The Study of Chemical Composition** (1904). This work gives an account of the methods used in examining this important topic up to the end of the 19th century.

R. B. Gordon, **A List of Books on the History of Science** (1945), 2nd Supplement, Part 5, **Chemistry, Crystallography and Mineralogy.**

A. Ladenburg, **Lectures on the History and Development of Chemistry since the time of Lavoisier,** translated by *L. Dobbin* (1900). An excellent account of early chemistry.

T. Martin Lowry, **Historical Introduction to Chemistry** (1915). A good medium length text useful up to the date of issue.

E. von Meyer, **A History of Chemistry,** translated by *G. McGowan*, (3rd Edition 1906).

R. H. Murray, **Science and Scientists in the Nineteenth Century** (1925).

M. Ornstein, **The Role of Scientific Societies in the 17th Century,** (3rd Edition 1939).

J. R. Partington, **Origins and Development of Applied Chemistry.** A massive and outstandingly valuable work with much

bibliographical detail of the early history of industrial chemistry.
M. M. Pattison Muir, **A History of Chemical Theories.** A
valuable account of the work of the 18th and 19th centuries.
R. B. Pilcher, **A Century of Chemistry - from Boyle to Priestley**
(1940), an R.I.C. monograph. A study of early history.
W. Ramsay, **Essays, Biographical and Chemical** (1908). This
is focussed mainly on the early chemists.
W. Ramsay, **Life and Letters of Joseph Black M.D.** (1918).
The introduction by *F. G. Donnan* gives, in addition, an excel-
lent account of the life of *Sir W. Ramsay*.
G. Sarton, **Introduction to the History of Science.** Three
volumes of this enormous treatise have appeared:-

1. 1927. From Homer to Omar Khayyam.
2. 1935. From Rabbi ben Ezra to Roger Bacon.
3. 1947-1948. In two parts.
    Science and Learning in the 14th Century.

This treatise deals in great detail with the origins and history
of all forms of scientific thought.
T. E. Thorpe, **Sir Henry Enfield Roscoe** (1916). Not only a
fascinating biography of Roscoe, but also a valuable commentary
on his influence on current chemical development.
T. E. Thorpe, **Essays in Historical Chemistry** (1902). Short
lives of famous chemists.
T. E. Thorpe, **A History of Chemistry** (2 Vols., 1921).
W. A. Tilden, **The Progress of Scientific Discovery in our own
times; with Biographical Notices** (2nd Edition, 1913). Although semi-popular in style, it is of great interest to the
chemical historian.
W. A. Tilden, **Chemical Invention and Discovery in the Twentieth
Century** (1916). A popular work, intended for the general
reader, but a clear and well-illustrated book, not without value
to the student.
W. A. Tilden, **Famous Chemists, the Men and their Work** (1921).
Another series of short lives, so arranged as to give an historical account of chemistry and its theories.
V. Volhardt, **Justus von Liebig** (2 Vols., 1909). No student of
chemical history can omit the study of the life and influence of
Liebig, one of the founders of organic chemistry as we know it.
M. E. Weekes, **The Discovery of the Elements** (5th Edition,

1948). A fascinating, well-documented and historically sound account of the discovery of the elements.

L. M. *Woodruff (Editor)*, **Development of the Sciences** (1941).

4.2. Analytical Chemistry. Treatises and monographs on analytical chemistry abound; the main types are illustrated by the examples set out in the sections below.

4.21. General Industrial Analysis.
Allen's Commercial Organic Analysis (5th Edition, 10 Vols., 1933-1937), edited by *C. A. Mitchell, S. S. Sadtler and E. C. Lathrop.* This is a collection of methods of analysis of organic materials appearing in commerce. Much of the information is concerned with foods and drugs and the work might have been included in Section 4.22. The information of this work is becoming a little outmoded, but is, in general, reliable.

G. Lunge and C. A. Keane, **Technical Methods of Chemical Analysis**, (4 Vols., 2nd Edition, 1924). This work deals with heavy chemicals and tar products, etc., and is largely a collection of routine methods for analytical control in these industries.

F. D. Snell and F. M. Biffen, **Commercial Methods of Analysis**, 1944. Largely relates to industrial control methods in the heavy chemical, pigment, paint, varnish and rubber industries.

Mention should also be made in this section of the monthly **Analytica Chimica Acta**, a journal for original communications in analytical chemistry, Vol. 1 appeared in 1947, and each annual volume is published in six parts.

B. L. Clarke and I. M. Kolthoff (Editors), **Chemical Analysis.** A series of specialist volumes on various types of analytical techniques.

- Vol. 1. *M. B. Jacobs,* The **Analytical Chemistry of Industrial Poisons, Hazards and Solvents** (1949).
- Vol. 2. *H. H. Strain,* **Chromatographic Adsorption Analysis** (1945).
- Vol. 3. *E. B. Sandell,* **Colorimetric Determination of Traces of Metals** (1950).
- Vol. 4. *J. F. Flagg,* **Organic Reagents used in Gravimetric and Volumetric Analysis** (1948).
- Vol. 5. *J. Mitchell and D. M. Smith,* **Aquametry** (1948).
- Vol. 6. *R. H. Mueller,* **Analytical Instruments and Techniques** (1956).

Vol. 7. *M. B. Jacobs and L. Scheflan*, **Chemical Analysis of Industrial Solvents** (1953).

I. M. Kolthoff and V. A. Stenger, **Volumetric Analysis**, Vol. 1. Theoretical Fundamentals (1942); Vol. 2. Titration methods (1947); Vol. 3. Oxidation-reduction methods (1951).

J. L. Lingane, **Electroanalytical Chemistry** (1953).

W. Fresenius and G. Jauder, **Handbuch der analytischen Chemie.** A series of volumes dealing with the determination of elements and radicles. There are eight 'volumes' each in various parts.

P. W. Mullen, **Modern Gas Analysis** (1955).

4.22. Foods and Drugs.

As there are legal standards for many foods and drugs, and as their sale and quality are controlled by the Foods and Drugs Acts, a special literature has grown up round their analysis. Examples of standard works in this field are:-

Official and Tentative Methods of the A.O.A.C. (6th Edition, 1945). The standard modes of examination of foods and agricultural materials officially recognized in the U.S.A.

Standard Methods of the Examination of Dairy Products; (Microbiological, bioassay and chemical). Published by the *American Public Health Association* (1941).

H. E. Cox, **The Chemical Analysis of Foods** (4th Edition, 1950).

N. Evers and G. D. Elsdon, **Analysis of Drugs and Chemicals,** (1929).

H. D. Richmond, G. D. Elsdon and G. H. Walker, **Dairy Chemistry** (1942).

A. L. and K. B. Winton, **The Structure and Composition of Food** (4 Vols., 1932). Deals fully with all types of foods and beverages.

D. Glick (Editor), **Methods of Biochemical Analysis** (3 Vols., 1954-1955.

K. Lang and E. Lehnartz, **Handbuch der physiologisch und pathologisch-chemischen Analyse.** A series of Volumes.

4.23. Organic Analytical Procedures.

Apart from micro-analytical techniques (Section 4.24) the majority of works in this field relate to the identification of organic compounds and to the use of organic reagents in inorganic analysis, as, for example:-

J. F. Flagg, **Organic Reagents** (1948).

F. J. Welcher, **Organic Analytical Reagents** (1947).
E. H. Huntress and S. P. Mulliken, **Identification of Pure Organic Compounds** (1941).
E. H. Huntress, **The Preparation, Properties, Chemical Behaviour and Identification of Organic Chlorine Compounds** (1948).
J. Mitchell, I. M. Kolthoff, E. S. Proskauer, A. Weissberger (Editors), **Organic Analysis.** A series of volumes on quantitative organic analysis. Vol. 1, 1953; Vol. 2,

The two latter works are of great value as compendia for the identification of organic compounds.

4·24. Microchemical and Semimicrochemical Methods.

These works resolve themselves into two classes, those dealing with the micro- and semimicro- estimation of the elements and specific groups of organic compounds, and those dealing with the colorimetric and turbidimetric detection and estimation of trace ions. Examples are:-

F. Feigl, **Qualitative Analysis by Spot Tests** (3rd Edition, 1947). A comprehensive survey by a scientist largely responsible for introducing these methods.
J. Lindner, **Mikromass analytische Bestimmung des Kohlenstoffes und Wasserstoffes** (1941).
L. and A. Kofler, **Mikro-methoden** (1948).
R. F. Milton and W. A. Waters, **Methods of Quantitative Microanalysis** (1949).
A. A. Benedetti-Pichler, **Introduction to the Microtechnique of Inorganic Analysis** (1942).
H. V. A. Briscoe and P. F. Holt, **Inorganic Microanalysis** (1950).
J. B. and V. Niederl, **Micromethods of Quantitative Organic Analysis** (2nd Edition, 1942).
F. Pregl and J. Grant, **Quantitative Organic Microanalysis** (4th English Edition, 1946). A linear successor of the original work by *Pregl* on this subject.
F. Welcher, **Organic Analytical Reagents** (4 Vols., 1947-1948).

4·25. Specialized Topics of Analytical Chemistry.

A vast number of specialized monographs are available on the application of analytical procedures to a limited field, such as vitamin assays, or the determination of water; or on the application of particular principles, usually physical methods e.g. polarography. Only a few examples can be given:-

Association of Vitamin Chemists, **Methods of Vitamin Assay** (1947).
H. T. S. Britton, Conductometric Analysis (1934).
T. R. P. Gibb, **Optical Methods of Chemical Analysis** (1942).
G. Klein, **Handbuch der Pflanzenanalyse** (4 Vols. in 6 parts, 1931).
J. Mitchell and D. M. Smith, **Aquametry** (1948).
H. J. Sand, **Electrochemistry and Electrochemical Analysis** (3 Vols., 1939).
H. H. Strain, **Chromatographic Adsorption Analysis** (1942).
W. L. Gore, **Statistical Methods for Chemical Experimentation** (1952). A textbook of statistical concepts applied to analytical procedures.

4·26. General Analytical Chemistry.

There are many works, also, dealing with the general methods of analysis, and improvements in such techniques as weighing, computation etc., which are common to all fields of analysis. Of such are:-

R. E. Burk and O. Grummitt, **Recent Advances in Analytical Chemistry** (1949). This has the same title, but no other obvious connexion with the 2 Vols. published by *C. A. Mitchell* in 1931.
T. B. Crumpler and J. H. Yoe, **Chemical Computations and Errors** (1940).
F. D. and C. T. Snell, **Colorimetric Methods of Analysis** (2nd Edition, 2 Vols., 1936).
F. P. Treadwell and W. T. Hall, **Quantitative Analysis** (9th Edition, 1942). This work, together with a work of the same title by *Clowes and Coleman*, has been the general basis of training in chemical analysis in this country.
W. W. Scott, **Standard Methods of Chemical Analysis** (2 Vols., 5th Edition, 1939). A well known American standard text.

4·3. Inorganic and Physical Chemistry.

In 1817-1819 *Gmelin* published his **Handbuch der theoretischen Chemie.** This work (its title should be considered equivalent to **Handbook of Pure Chemistry**) proved popular and ran through five editions in fifty years, whilst a translation by *H. Watts* was prepared and published by the *Cavendish Society* between

1848-1872, in 19 Vols. The sixth and seventh editions, the former of which commenced publication in 1872, were edited by *Kraut*, and at that time the work was known as *Gmelin-Kraut*. The publication was taken over in 1921 by the *Deutsche Chemischen Gesellschaft*, although parts of the seventh edition were still outstanding, and the work is still being continued under the editorship of *Dr. Pietsch* at the *Gmelin Institute* at Clausthal-Zellerfeld. The present title is **Handbuch der anorganischen Chemie.**

Unfortunately, this reference-work, although exhaustive and accurate, is incomplete; there are some elements for which no recent volumes have appeared, and others are seriously out-of-date. In spite of this *Gmelin* is one of the accepted reference works for inorganic chemistry, although it does not, in quite the same way as *Beilstein*, dominate the literature of its field. The list of volumes available, with their publication dates is given below:-

System No.	Element	Part	Year
1	Edelgase	–	1926
2	Wasserstoff	–	1927
3	Sauerstoff	1	1943
4	Stickstoff	1	1934
		2	1935
		3	1936
		4	1936
5	Fluor	–	1926
6	Chlor	–	1927
7	Brom	–	1931
8	Jod	1	1931
		2	1933
9	Schwefel	1	1942
10	Selen A	1	1942
	Selen B	1	1949
11	Tellur	–	1940
12	Polonium und Isotope	–	1941
13	Bor	–	1926
18	Antimon A	1	1942
		2	1943
	Antimon B	1	1943

System No.	Element	Part	Year
18	Antimon B	2	1949
19	Wismut	–	1927
20	Lithium	–	1927
21	Natrium	–	1928
22	Kalium	1	1936
		2	1937
		3	1937
		4	1937
		5	1938
		6	1938
		7	1938
	Anhangband		1942
23	Ammonium	1	1936
		2	1936
24	Rubidium	–	1937
25	Cæsium	1	1938
		2	1938
26	Beryllium	–	1930
27	Magnesium A	1	1937
		2	1937
		3	1942
	Magnesium B	1	1937
		2	1938
		3	1938
		4	1939
29	Strontium	–	1931
30	Barium	–	1932
31	Radium und Isotope	–	1928
32	Zink	–	1924
33	Cadmium	–	1925
35	Aluminium A	1	1934
		2	1934
		3	1936
		4	1936
		5	1937
		6	1939
		7	1941
	Aluminium B	1	1933
		2	1934

System No.	Element	Part	Year
36	Gallium	–	1936
37	Indium	–	1936
38	Thallium	1	1939
		2	1940
		3	1940
39	Seltene Erde	1	1938
40	Actinium und Isotope	–	1942
43	Hafnium	–	1941
45	Germanium	–	1931
51	Protactinium	–	1942
53	Molybdan	–	1935
54	Wolfram	–	1933
55	Uran	–	1936
58	Kobalt A	1	1931
		2	1932
	Kobalt B	–	1930
59	Eisen A	1	1929
		2	1929
		3	1930
		4	1932
		5	1933
		6	1934
		7	1934
		8	1936
		9	1939
	Eisen B	1	1929
		2	1930
		3	1930
		4	1931
		5	1932
	Eisen C	1	1937
		2	1939
	Eisen D	–	1936
	Ergänzungsband		1937
	Eisen F I	1	1939
		2	1941
	Eisen F II	1	1938
		2	1939
63	Ruthenium	–	1938

System No.	Element	Part	Year
64	Rhodium	–	1938
65	Palladium	1	1941
		2	1942
66	Osmium	–	1939
67	Iridium	–	1939
68	Platin A	1	1938
		2	1939
		3	1939
		4	1940
		5	1949
	Platin B	1	1939
		2	1939
		3	1939
		4	1942
	Platin C	1	1939
		2	1940
		3	1940
69	Masurium	–	1941
70	Rhenium	–	1941

Patentsammlungen

System No.	Element	Part	Year
27	Magnesium-Legierungen	–	1937
32	Zink-Legierungen	1/1	1943
		1/2	1943
		2/1	1943
		2/2	1943
35	Aluminium-Legierungen	1	1936
		2	1936
	Ergänzungsband I	1	1939
		2	1939
		3	1939
57	Nickel-Legierungen	1	1943
		2	1943
59	Eisen-Stahl-Legierungen	1	1932
	Ergänzungsband I	–	1935
	Ergänzungsband II	1	1940
		2	1940
68	Platinmetalle Leg.	–	1937

J. W. Mellor, **A Comprehensive Treatise on Inorganic and Theoretical Chemistry** (16 Vols., published from 1922-1937). This is still the most satisfactory text that has been produced on inorganic chemistry in the English language, and it is to be brought up-to-date by a series of supplementary volumes completing the survey of the literature up to 1950.   The first of these supplementary volumes (Suppt. II, Part 1, The Halogens) appeared in 1956; other volumes are in the press.

J. Newton Friend, **A Textbook of Inorganic Chemistry** (12 Vols., 1914-1938). This series is conceived on a somewhat less exhaustive scale than that of *Mellor* but, nevertheless, constitutes a very useful reference work. It contains, in particular, excellent surveys of the organo-metallic compounds, and of the organic compounds of phosphorus, not within the scope of *Mellor.*

R. Abegg and A. Auerbach, **Handbuch der anorganischen Chemie** (7 Vols., 1905-1921).

O. Dammer, **Handbuch der anorganischen Chemie** (5 Vols., 1892-1903). This and the former work are now only of historical interest; *Dammer* was originally the inorganic counterpart of *Beilstein,* but it has not persisted. Both *Abegg* and *Dammer* are concise, and within their temporal limitations, covered the subject matter adequately.

K. Hoffmann, **Lexikon der anorganischen Chemie** (3 Vols., 1912-1925). The intention was that this should become a reference dictionary of inorganic compounds comparable with the **Lexikon** of *Richter* for organic compounds. Unfortunately, it was never taken beyond the first four volumes.

H. Moissan, **Traité de Chimie minerale,** was originally issued in 5 Vols. (1904-1906), but has been succeeded by a new edition in 12 Vols., under the editorship of *Paul Pascal* and *P. Baud.* This series is probably the most modern and complete of existing treatises on inorganic chemistry and was published during 1931-1934. The matter is arranged in an unusual fashion:-

Vol. 1. Air, water, hydrogen, oxygen, ozone and the halogens.

Vol. 2. Sulphur, selenium and tellurium, the sulphuric acid industry.

Vol. 3. Nitrogen, phosphorus and arsenic.

Vol. 4. Antimony, bismuth, vanadium, niobium, tantalum

and boron.

Vol. 5. Carbon, fuels, silicon, titanium, germanium, zirconium and ammonium.

Vol. 6a. Alkali metals.

Vol. 6b. Alkaline earth metals.

Vol. 7. Beryllium, magnesium, zinc, cadmium, aluminium, gallium, indium, cements and ceramics.

Vol. 8. Rare earth elements, copper, silver, gold and mercury.

Vol. 9. Tin, lead, thallium, manganese, rhenium and iron.

Vol. 10. Nickel, cobalt and chromium.   Complexes.

Vol. 11. Molybdenum, tungsten, uranium and thorium.   Platinum metals.

Vol. 12. Rare gases, alloys and radioactive elements.

Like most French compendia, the work lacks a good index, but is well documented. It is, of course, the inorganic counterpart of *Grignard's* Traité de Chimie organique.

H. E. Roscoe and C. Schorlemmer, A Treatise on Chemistry. This was first published in 1877, and several editions of the two volumes on metallic and non-metallic elements have been published. Although the work is now out-of-date, the matter is sound, well-written and can be read with profit even now, as the factual basis of inorganic chemistry changes very slowly.

Among other works, conceived on a less extensive scale the following may be mentioned:-

F. Ephraim (translated by *P. C. L. Thorne and E. R. Roberts*), Inorganic Chemistry (5th Edition, 1948). This is probably one of the most valuable single volumes on the subject.

J. R. Partington, Textbook of Inorganic Chemistry (1937). A valuable teaching text.

E. Remy (translated by *J. S. Anderson and J. Kleinberg*), Inorganic Chemistry (Vol. 1, 1955). Presents inorganic chemistry in the modern way.

E. B. Maxted, Modern Advances in Inorganic Chemistry (1947). The title of this work is sufficiently indicative of its subject matter.

H. F. Walton, Inorganic Preparations (1948).

H. S. Booth and W. C. Fernelius, Inorganic Syntheses, Vols. I, II and III; 1939, 1946, 1950. These works are intended to offer tested methods for the economical preparation of inorganic substances, and the three latter are comparable to **Organic Syntheses,** although they are much less extensive.

N. V. Sidgwick, **The Chemical Elements and their Compounds** (2 Vols., 1950). This is a masterly survey of the principles underlying the chemistry of inorganic structures. It deals, incidentally, with the chemistry, and structure, of carbon considered as an element.

4.33. Physical Chemistry.

Among the host of books on physical chemistry in its various phases, there are many monographs but few compendia or 'omnibus' works. This is probably due to the fact that physical chemistry is more speculative and less factual than other branches. Among the larger works are:-

J. Newton Friend, **Textbook of Physical Chemistry** (Vol. 1, 1932; Vol. 2, 1935). This work gives a clear and adequate introduction to many of the fields.

J. R. Partington, **An Advanced Treatise on Physical Chemistry,** a work in five volumes:-

Vol. 1. Fundamental Principles and the Properties of Gases (1949).

Vol. 2. Properties of Liquids (1951).

Vol. 3. Properties of Solids (1952).

Vol. 4. Physico-chemical Optics (1953).

Vol. 5. Molecular Spectra and Structure; Dielectrics and Dipole Moments (1954).

This is probably the best general text on these branches of the subject. It is not proposed to give a long series of examples of the monographs on physical chemical topics; such special subjects as kinetics, quantum mechanics, fluorescence, electrolytic dissociation, corrosion etc., have their own abundant literature. The following, however, may be noted:-

R. E. Burk and O. Grummitt (Editors), **Major Instruments of Science and their Application** (1945). Deals with electron diffraction, electron microscopy, *X*-ray diffraction, infra-red and chemical spectroscopy.

R. E. Burk and O. Grummitt (Editors), **Chemical Architecture** (1948).

I. M. Kolthoff and J. J. Lingane, **Polarography** (2nd Edition, 2 Vols., 1952).

A. J. Rutgers, **Physical Chemistry** (1954). A textbook of modern physicochemical theory.

E. I. Rabinowitch, **Photosynthesis.**

Vol. 1. Chemistry of Photosynthesis (1945).
Vol. II, Part 1. Physical Chemistry, Kinetics and Spectroscopy of Photosynthesis, (1951).
Vol. II, Part 2. Kinetics of Photosynthesis (1955).

4·4. Mineral and Metallurgical Chemistry.

The usual broad division is made between ferrous and non-ferrous metallurgy, and it is usual to find the more important works devoted to one or other of these fields, but not both. There are no large compendia on metallurgy, and the following are two typical examples of the larger volumes available on the subject:-

M. Teichert, **Ferrous Metallurgy** (3 Vols., 1944).

F. Liddell, **Handbook of Non-ferrous Metallurgy** (2nd Edition, 2 Vols., 1945). Either of these works will give a useful bibliography of their respective divisions.

Multiplication of examples of the monographs on a borderland subject is unsuitable in a small volume such as this, but some mention should be made of **Metallurgical Abstracts,** published monthly with the **Journal of the Institute of Metals,** and **Abstracts of Current Literature** (which are issued monthly with the **Journal of the Iron and Steel Institute**). A careful study of the book-notices in each of these abstracts series will give a good survey of the latest contributions to the monograph literature.

4·5. Biochemistry.

The literature of biochemistry is widely diffused and is difficult to search, largely owing to its being a borderland subject. There are many monographs, too numerous to catalogue here, and much biochemical information is to be found in the chemical and physiological literature. The diffuseness of biochemical literature is to some extent mitigated by the publication of annual reviews of progress in various of the subsections of biochemistry; some of these volumes are mentioned in Section 4·7.

Of the major compendia, the following are the most important and detailed:-

E. Abderhalden, the great **Biochemisches Handlexicon** originally published in 7 Vols. between 1911-1912, to which 8 supplementary volumes have been added, making 15 in all, and covering the literature up to 1933. This work takes as its terms of reference all compounds having connexion with life processes, which means an arbitrary selection of material from organic chemistry. The work is fully documented.

E. Abderhalden, **Handbuch der biologischen Arbeitsmethoden.** Parts of this great work appeared in 1910 and in subsequent years, up to 1930. It contains accounts of all types of biochemical laboratory procedures, and is really a collection of treatises by various authors.

Biochemical Preparations, started in 1949, has published four Vols. This is to be a series of volumes comparable with **Organic Syntheses.**

L. Vallez (Editor), **Substances Naturelles de Synthèse.** A series of preparative directions for the economic laboratory synthesis of naturally occurring substances. The works also have extensive commentaries on the chemistry of the reactions involved. Ten volumes (1951-1956) have been issued; they are of considerable practical value.

E. Chargaff and J. N. Davidson, **The Nucleic Acids**, Vols. 1 and 2 (1955).

J. B. Sumner and K. Myrbäck, **The Enzymes** (2 Vols., 1951 and 1952). Each volume is in two parts and the whole constitutes a survey of the biochemistry and technology of enzymes.

S. P. Colowick and N. O. Kaplan, **Methods in Enzymology.**

Vol. 1. Preparation and Assay of Enzymes (1955).
Vol. 2. Preparation and Assay of Enzymes (contd.) (1955).
Vol. 3. Preparation and Assay of Substrates (1956).
Vol. 4. Special Techniques (1956).

G. Pincus and K. V. Thimann, **The Hormones** (3 Vols., 1953-5).
H. Neurath and K. Bailey, **The Proteins** (2 Vols. each in two parts, 1953-1954).
W. H. Sebrell and R. S. Harris, **The Vitamins** (3 Vols., 1954).

4·6. Organic Chemistry.

The most extensive reference work on organic chemistry is

Beilstein's **Handbuch der organischen Chemie.** There have been four editions of this work; the first (2 Vols., 1881-1883) and second (3 Vols., 1886-1890) were produced by *Beilstein* without more than nominal assistance, and he used only one assistant to produce the third edition in 1893-1899. *Jacobson* produced a supplementary volume in 1906.

The fourth or present edition was commenced in 1918, and Vol. 27 appeared in 1937 (Vols. 28 and 29 are indexes, and appeared in 1938-1940). This is the **Hauptwerk** or main series of volumes, and covers the literature up to the end of 1909. The first and second supplements carry the work to 1919 and 1929 respectively.

The first supplement in 15 actual volumes, is complete and was published over the period 1928-1938, *i.e.* the publication of the first supplement overtook that of the main volumes, and the indexes cover both **Hauptwerk** and **Erstes Ergänzungswerk**. It should be kept in mind that the second supplement describes many substances not mentioned in either the main work or first supplement; these do not, of course, appear in the main index.

The second supplement commenced publication in 1941 and is now complete.

The third supplement covering two decades (1930-1949) is now well under way and the first volume (1a) appeared in 1957. It will be much larger than the previous supplements, for not only does it cover a double period, but the period was very productive.

References to *Beilstein* are often met in terms of H, E I or E II, referring to the **Hauptwerk** and **Erstes** or **Zweites Ergänzungswerk** respectively. The classification of compounds in *Beilstein* is based on a special system; this is a little difficult for beginners to follow and recourse may be had to an excellent publication of *E. H. Huntress*, entitled **A Brief Introduction to the Use of Beilstein's Handbuch der organischen Chemie.**

Whilst *Beilstein* dominates the literature of organic chemistry, there are many other very valuable publications some of which are:-

M. M. Richter, **Lexikon der Kohlenstoff-Verbindungen.** *Beilstein's* first three editions had no formula index, and *Richter*

supplied this want in the form of a **Lexikon** in which the substances are arranged in order of their molecular formulæ. The entry also gives the main physical properties, references to the original literature, and to the appropriate pages in the third edition of *Beilstein*. The first edition of *Richter* appeared in 1884, and the third edition, in four volumes, completes the literature up to 1909. The publication of *Richter* then ended and was supplemented by
R. Stelzner, **Literatur-Register der organischen Chemie** of which the following volumes were published:-

1. 1910-1911.
2. 1912-1913.
3. 1914-1915.
4. 1916-1918.
5. 1919-1921.

At this point, publication of *Stelzner* ceased and the whole project was merged in the formula indexes to **Chemisches Zentralblatt.** It will be realized that *Stelzner* was not an exact continuation of *Richter* in the old style; the former gives more detail; nor is the formula index of **Chemisches Zentralblatt** an exact continuation of *Stelzner*.

Various abridged compendia, which are representative rather than exhaustive, are much used by organic chemists.

V. Grignard (Editor). **Traité de chimie organique,** which comprises 22 Vols. is not an exhaustive compendium, like *Beilstein*. It is conceived on a large scale, but does not claim to be complete. *Grignard* states that 'it is written in the didactic form, inspired by modern theories and sufficiently developed to conform to the actual requirements of the research chemist'. It is, therefore, to be regarded as a detailed account of organic chemistry, as opposed to an account of organic compounds. The subject matter is arranged in an unusual manner, but the work has a collective index volume which is very comprehensive.
M. Faraday, **An Encyclopædia of Hydrocarbon Compounds.** This is an attempt to provide an expanding compendium of hydrocarbon information, on the loose-leaf basis. The first 12 Vols. have been issued in the period 1944-1954, and in them the material is arranged in ascending order of carbon number; these volumes cover the range C_1 to C_{12} and supplementary

pages have been issued for some volumes bringing them up-to-date; in addition, a second edition of Vol. 1 was issued in two parts in 1950, Part 1a covering C_1 to C_3 while Part 1b deals with C_4 to C_5.

F. Radt (Editor), **Elsevier's Encyclopædia of Organic Chemistry.** This work has been planned, like *Beilstein,* on the grand scale, and has, so far, issued about one quarter of the series of volumes. There are to be twenty volumes in all, but some volumes will be issued in parts so that the actual number of issues is, as yet, undetermined. The plan is somewhat different from that of *Beilstein;* some of the physiological data relating to organic compounds are given, and there are also schematic representations of the formulæ and reactions of groups of compounds. The literature cover is such that in Vol. 13, for example, 'the literature up to and including 1936 has been consulted and the literature concerning the structure of compounds up to 1947'. The bibliographical cover up to 1936 is extensive, but not complete; no account is taken of chemical patent literature.

V. Richter, **The Chemistry of Carbon Compounds.** This work has gone through twelve German editions and is now available, translated into English, in four volumes:-

Vol. 1. 1934. The aliphatic series.
Vol. 2. 1939. The alicyclic compounds and natural products.
Vol. 3. 1946. The aromatic compounds.
Vol. 4. 1947. The heterocyclic compounds.

It has been an invaluable desk-book for organic chemists and is recommended for general reference where a detailed search is not required, but is now largely replaced by

E. H. Rodd (Editor), **Chemistry of Carbon Compounds.** A series of volumes rather more detailed than *Richter* but fully modern and resembling *Richter* in arrangement. The following have appeared:-

Vol. 1, Part A. General Introduction and Aliphatic Compounds (1951).
Vol. 1, Part B. Aliphatic Compounds (1952).
Vol. 2, Part A. Alicyclic Compounds (1953).
Vol. 2, Part B. Alicyclic Compounds (1953).
Vol. 3, Part A. Aromatic Compounds (1954).

Vol. 3, Part B. Aromatic Compounds (1956).

There is to be a Vol. 4 in two parts describing the heterocyclic compounds and a fifth volume for miscellaneous compounds and Indexes.

I. M. Heilbron and H. M. Bunbury, **Dictionary of Organic Compounds.** The sub-title of this work (4 Vols., 3rd Edition 1954), **– The Constitution, Physical and Chemical Properties of the Principal Carbon Compounds, together with the Relevant Literature References** – gives some idea of the purpose of the work which describes some 28,000 compounds and gives selected references to their preparation. The matter being presented in a very accessible form, this concise reference work is a valuable short cut in literature searching, when the necessity for exhaustive data does not arise. Under each entry, there will usually be found a reference to one good method of preparation.

V. Meyer and P. Jacobson, **Lehrbuch der organischen Chemie.** Such compendia as have already been described are to be regarded as of properties, rather than as of methods. Whereas others describe the chemistry of compounds, *Meyer and Jacobson* is more a book of the methods of organic chemistry, and is illustrated by a wealth of examples and references. It is scarcely as up-to-date as could be desired, part having been published in 1902. The publication plan is:-

Vol. 1 Part 1 1907
Vol. 1 Part 2 1913
Vol. 2 Part 1 1902
Vol. 2 Part 2 1903
Vol. 2 Part 3 1920

Supplementary volumes were issued in
1924 and 1929.

E. A. Braude and F. C. Nachod, **Determination of Organic Structures by Physical Methods** (1955). This gives a very useful survey of the subject and is well provided with references.

G. Egloff, **Physical Constants of Hydrocarbons.** Four volumes of this huge work have appeared (1939, 1940, 1946 and 1947):-

Vol. 1. Paraffins, olefins, acetylenes and other aliphatic hydrocarbons.

Vol. 2. Cyclanes, cyclenes, cyclynes and other alicyclic hydrocarbons.

Vol. 3. Mononuclear aromatic hydrocarbons.

Vol. 4. Polynuclear aromatic hydrocarbons.

J. Houben and T. Weyl, **Die Methoden der organischen Chemie.** In this publication much useful matter concerning basic methods and principles of organic chemistry is to be found. The third edition (4 Vols., 1925, 1925, 1930 and 1941) is that most commonly found in libraries, although it has been out of print for several years. The fourth edition is now in active preparation. Some twelve volumes, several in separate parts are expected. The following are presently published:-

Vol. I	General methods
Vol. II	Analytical methods.
Vol. III/1 and III/2	Physical methods.
Vol. IV/2	Catalysis.
Vol. VII/1	Aldehydes.
Vol. VIII	Oxygen compounds.
Vol. IX	Sulphur, Se and Te compounds.
Vol. XI/1	Nitrogen compounds.

H. Gilman (Editor), **Organic Chemistry; an Advanced Treatise,** 4 Vols. (I and II, 2nd Edition 1943; III and IV 1953). An excellent survey of the subject, topic by topic, each chapter being written by an authority on the subject.

A. Weissberger (Editor), **Technique of Organic Chemistry.** A series of valuable volumes dealing with the methods of organic chemical analysis and reaction. The volume titles are:-

Vol. 1. Physical methods of organic chemistry.

Vol. 2. Catalytic photochemical and electrolyte reactions.

Vol. 3. Unit processes.

Vol. 4. Distillation.

Vol. 5. Adsorption and chromatography.

Vol. 6. Micro and semimicro methods.

Vol. 7. Organic solvents.

Vol. 8. Investigation of rates and mechanisms of reaction.

Vol. 9. Chemical applications of spectroscopy.

G. M. Dyson, **A Manual of Organic Chemistry** (Vol. I, 1950). An advanced textbook for senior students and graduates specializing in organic research.

There are several series of volumes entirely devoted to the preparative side of organic chemistry. An example of such is **Organic Syntheses** which, as its sub-title indicates, is an **Annual Publication of Satisfactory Methods for the Preparation of Organic Chemicals.** This invaluable publication, now in its thirty-sixth year, is exactly what it is claimed to be, a recipe-book for organic chemists, in which each set of directions has been tested independently by two skilled chemists, apart from the author of the recipe. Collective volumes which embody the annual volumes 1-9, 10-19 and 20-29 are available, in which the recipes are arranged in alphabetical order. Among other important works on organic chemistry may be mentioned:-

L. Vanino, **Handbuch der präparative Chemie,** which has reached its third edition (Vol. 1, Inorganic, 1925; Vol. 2, Organic, 1937) gives preparative details for many chemicals not yet covered by **Organic Syntheses.**

Roger Adams (Chairman of Editorial Board), **Organic Reactions.** Commencing with 1942 nine volumes of this series have been issued; each volume discusses a number of reactions (approximately twelve) each of them being fully documented, giving the history, applications and mechanism of the reaction. This is a valuable tool for the organic chemist desiring to study an individual reaction.

Newer Methods of Preparative Organic Chemistry. A series of papers published in **Die Chemie** (1940-1948) and reprinted in book form, giving details of modern preparative techniques.

W. Theilheimer, **Synthetic Methods of Organic Chemistry.** A series of nine volumes giving a systematic critical review of the current literature of new methods in organic chemistry. Vols. 1, 2 and 5-9 are in English; 3 and 4 in German.

A. Weissberger (Editor), **The Chemistry of Heterocyclic Compounds.** A survey of heterocyclic chemistry.

Vol. 1. *F. G. Mann,* Heterocyclic derivatives of P, As, Sb, Bi and Si (1950).

Vol. 2. *C. F. H. Allen et al.,* Six membered heterocyclic nitrogen compounds with four condensed rings (1951).

Vol. 3. *H. D. Hartough et al.,* Thiophene and its derivatives (1952).

Vol. 4. *L. L. Bambas,* Five-membered heterocyclic compounds containing N and S, or N, S and O (1952).

Vol. 5. *J. C. E. Simpson*, Condensed pridazine and pyrazine rings (1953). Vol. 6. *K. Hofmann*, Imidazole and derivs., Part I. (1953). Vol. 7. *H. D. Hartough & S. L. Meisel*, Compounds with condensed thiophene rings (1954). Vol. 8. *W. Sumpter & F. M. Miller*, Indole and carbazole systems (1954). Vol. 9. *R. M. Acheson*, Acridines (1956). Vol. 10. *J. G. Erikson at al.*, Triazines, tetrazines and pentazines (1956). Vol. 11. D. G. I. *Felton & G. A. Swan*, Phenazines (1957).

R. C. Elderfeld (Editor), **Heterocyclic Compounds.** A series of volumes of which the following have appeared:-

Vol. 1. 3-, 4-, 5- and 6-membered monocyclic compounds with one O, N or S atom. Vol. 2. Polycyclic 5- and 6-membered compounds with one O or S atom. Vol. 3. Polycyclic pyrrole derivs. and pyrindines. Vol. 4. Quinoline, *iso*quinoline and their benzo-derivs.. Vol. 5. 5-membeted systems with two hetero-atoms and their benzo derivs.. Vol. 6. 6-membered analogs of Vol. 5. Vol. 7. Heterocyclic compounds containing three hetero-atoms in 5-membered rings.

Hans Meyer, **Synthese der Kohlenstoff Verbindungen,** is a useful compendium published in 4 Vols., (2 sections each of two parts; 1938 and 1943) and constitutes a kind of dictionary with a short indication of the modes of synthesis of compounds. A typical entry (from page 464) reads:-

　　o-**Benzyl toluol.** $C_6H_5CH_2C_6H_4CH_3$

　　　1. Toluol, MnO + H_2SO_4. Eq.[1]
　　　2. Toluol, benzylchlorid; Zn-staub, erhitzen. A: gering.[2]
　　　3. *o*-Xylylchlorid. Bzl. Zn-staub.[3]

　　　　[1] *Weiler*, Ber., 1900,33,464.
　　　　[2] *Zincke*, Ber., 1873,6,906.
　　　　[3] *Barbier*, Ber., 1874,7,1544.

N. V. Sidgwick, **Organic Chemistry of Nitrogen** (2nd Edition, 1937. Rewritten by *T. W. J. Taylor and H. Wilson Baker*). A survey of the chemical and structural problems associated with the nitrogenous organic compounds.

C. Hollins, **The Synthesis of Nitrogen Ring Compounds** (1924). This work deals with structures containing a single hetero-atom (nitrogen) and is now somewhat out-of-date, although it contains a useful survey of earlier material.

E. H. Huntress, **The Preparation, Properties, Chemical Behaviour and Identification of Organic Chlorine Compounds** (1948). In this volume 1329 individual chlorine compounds (*i.e.* those most commonly encountered) are described, each with a fully documented monograph.

Z. I. Kertesz, **The Pectic Substances** (1952), deals with the chemistry, biochemistry, botany, manufacture and functions and applications of pectins.

R. H. F. Manske and H. L. Holmes, **The Alkaloids** (5 Vols., 1950-1955). A complete survey of the whole alkaloid field. Extremely well documented.

4·7. Annual Reviews and similar volumes.

The value of annual reviews has been amply demonstrated by the **Annual Reports of the Progress of Chemistry** first issued by *The Chemical Society* in 1905 (covering the year 1904) under the editorship of *G. T. Morgan*. The preface to the first volume states 'the object of these Reports is to present an epitome of the principal definite steps in advance which have been accomplished in the preceding year', and this aim has been adhered to throughout. A collective index of Vols. 1-46; 1904-1949 was published in 1951. The corresponding **Annual Reports of the Progress of Applied Chemistry** published by the *Society of Chemical Industry*, dates from 1916 and has furnished a most valuable annual volume dealing with industrial chemistry.

More recently a number of annual volumes dealing with various facets of chemistry have appeared. Reference has already been made to **Organic Syntheses**, a typical example of such a publication. Others are:-

Annual Review of Nuclear Science. First published in 1952.

Annual Review of Biochemistry, has appeared each year since 1932 and contains important reports on the progress of biochemistry from year to year.

Annual Review of Microbiology. Published since 1947, has a moderate interest for chemists, especially those engaged in the medicinal chemical field.

Annual Reviews of Petroleum Technology, published first in 1935 by the *Institute of Petroleum*, is typical of many of the specialized annual reports dealing with aspects of applied chemistry. World War II seriously interrupted the issue of

many technological annual volumes, and in this particular
instance a composite volume covering the years 1941-1945 was
issued in 1947; a further volume bridging the intervening gap
has been published (1950).
Annual Review of Physical Chemistry. The volumes of this
series are 'designed to appraise critically recent research in
physical chemistry'. The first volume was published in 1950.
Annual Review of Plant Physiology. First published in 1950
has much of interest to the chemist on phytochemical topics.
Recent Progress in Hormone Research. Commencing with Vol.
1 in 1947, and Vols. 2 and 3 in 1948, Vol. 4 in 1949, this work
is scarcely 'annual' but gives from year to year important
summaries of work in this field.
Although also not annual in the regularity of publication, **Zech-
meister's Fortschritte der Chemie organischer Naturstoffe is** a
very valuable report on the progress of the chemistry of naturally occurring organic compounds. Ten volumes have appeared
since 1938 and it gives a thorough and fully documented survey
of this field.

Among others are:-

Physiological Reviews. Since 1920.
Advances in Protein Chemistry. Since 1944.
Advances in Carbohydrate Chemistry. Since 1945.
Advances in Enzymology and related subjects in Biochemistry.
Annually since 1941.

4.8. Applied Chemistry.

The literature of applied chemistry is very extensive for few
manufacturing processes are non-chemical in either nature or
control. The following are given as examples of the kind of
work which the student will find useful in exploring this
territory.
4.81. Oils, Fats and Waxes.
J. Lewkowitsch, **Chemical Technology and Analysis of oils,
fats and waxes** (6th Edition, 1921).
H. Bennett (Editor), **Commercial waxes: Natural and Synthetic.**
T.P. Hilditch, **The Chemical Constitution of Natural Fats** (2nd
Edition, 1947).
A.E. Bailey et al., (Editors), **Fats and Oils,** a series of monographs:-
    1. *A.E. Bailey,* Industrial oil and fat products.

2. *K. S. Markley,* Fatty acids.

3. *A. E. Bailey,* Melting and solidification of fats and fatty acids.

4. *A. E. Bailey,* Cottonseed and cottonseed products.

5. *K. S. Markley et al.,* Soybeans and soybean products (2 Vols.).

6. *J. Davidson et al.,* Soap manufacture.

4.82. Essential Oils.
E. Guenther, **The Essential Oils** (8 Vols., 1948-1955).
Sir J. L. Simonsen.

Vol. 1, with *L. N. Owen,* Simpler acyclic and monocyclic terpenes and their derivatives (1947).

Vol. 2, with *L. N. Owen,* Dicyclic terpenes and their derivatives (1949).

Vol. 3, with *D. H. R. Barton,* Sesquiterpenes and their derivatives (1952).

4.83. Food Chemistry.
M. B. Jacobs et al., (Editors), **The Chemistry and Technology of Food and Food Products** (2nd Edition), comprising:-

Vol. 1. Fundamentals, unit operations and quality control (1951).

Vol. 2. Foods (1951).

Vol. 3. Preservation (1951).

4.84. Resins, Rubbers, Plastics.
H. Mark, E. S. Proskauer and V. J. Frilette, **Resins-Rubbers-Plastics,** a literature service covering the chemical and patent literature. This series was started in 1942 and now has monthly issues each about 100 pages.

H. Mark and E. Proskauer, **The Science of Plastics,** Vol. 1 (1950). A source book covering the literature from 1942-1946.

E. R. Blout, Monomers (1951), a collection of data and procedures on the basic materials for the synthesis of fibres, plastics and rubbers. A loose-leaf publication with ring-binding.

H. Mark, C. S. Marvel, H. W. Melville and G. S. Whitby (Editors), **High Polymers.** A series of volumes.

Vol. 1. *H. Mark and G. S. Whitby,* Collected papers of *W. H. Carothers* (1940).

Vol. 2. *H. Mark and A. V. Tobolsky,* Physical chemistry of high polymeric systems (2nd Edition, 1950).

Vol. 3. *G. M. Burnett*, Mechanism of polymer reactions (1954).

Vol. 4. *K. H. Meyer*, Natural and synthetic high polymers (2nd Edition, 1950).

Vol. 5. *E. O. H. and H. Spurlin*, Cellulose and cellulose derivatives (2nd Edition, 1953).

Vol. 6. *T. Alfrey*, Mechanical behaviour of high polymers (1948).

Vol. 7. *T. S. Carswell*, Phenoplasts (1947).

Vol. 8. *T. Alfrey, J. J. Bohrer and H. Mark*, Copolymerization (1952).

Polymers.

R. Houwink, **Fundamentals of Synthetic Polymer Technology** (1949).

R. Houwink, **Elastomers and Plastomers.**

Vol. 1. General theory (1950).

Vol. 2. Manufacture, properties and applications (1949).

Vol. 3. Testing and analysis (1948).

Rubber.

P. Schidrowitz and T. R. Dawson, **History of the Rubber Industry** (1952).

A. Drakeley (Editor), **Rubber Technology, Annual Report on the Progress of.** Annually since 1937.

Plastics.

American Society for Testing Materials Standards, **Plastics, Specifications, Methods of Testing, Nomenclature, Definitions** (1950).

P. Morgan, **Plastics Progress.** (Papers given at the Plastics Convention, 1951).

R. S. Morrell (Editor), **Synthetic Resins and Allied Plastics.**

C. E. Schildknecht, **Vinyl and Related Polymers** (1952).

4·85. Industrial Hygiene.

F. A. Patty (Editor), **Industrial Hygiene and Toxicology** (Vol. 1, 1948; Vol. 2, 1949).

F. H. Goldman, **Chemical Methods in Industrial Hygiene** (1953).

4·86. Detergents and Textile Chemistry.

J. C. Harris, **Detergency** (1954).

A. M. Schwartz and J. W. Perry, **Surface Active Agents** (1949).

E. Knecht and J. B. Fothergill, **The Principles and Practice of**

Textile Printing (1952).
A. *Matthews*, Textile Fibers (1947).
H. C. *Speel*, Textile Chemicals and Auxiliaries (1952).

4.87. Petroleum.
American Society for Testing Materials Standards, Petroleum Products and Lubricants, methods of testing, specifications, definitions, etc. (1951).
W. J. *Gruse and D. R. Stevens,* The Chemical Technology of Petroleum (2nd Edition, 1942).
C. *Ellis,* The Chemistry of Petroleum Products (Vol. 1, 1934; Vol. 2, 1947).
R. F. *Goldstein,* The Petroleum Chemicals Industry (1943).
K. V. *Ness and A. van Westen,* Aspects of the Constitution of Mineral Oils (1951).
A. E. *Dunstan, A. W. Nash, B. T. Brooks and H. T. Tizard (Editors),* A Comprehensive Treatise of the Principles and Practice of the Production and Refining of Mineral Oil (4 Vols. 1938-1939).

4.88. Paper.
C. *Dorée,* The Methods of Cellulose Chemistry (1947).
J. *Grant,* A Laboratory Handbook of Pulp and Paper Manufacture (1942).
J. *Grant,* Wood Pulp and Allied Products (2nd Edition, 1947).
E. *Hägglund,* Chemistry of Wood (1951).
P. H. *Hermans,* Physics and Chemistry of Cellulose Fibres (1949).
E. J. *Labane,* Dictionary and Encyclopædia of Paper and Paper-making (2nd Edition, 1952). This has a polyglot dictionary of papermaking terms with their equivalents in English, French, German, Dutch, Italian, Spanish and Swedish.
J. N. *Stephenson (Editor),* Pulp and Paper Manufacture, Vol. 1. Preparation and treatment of wood pulp (1952), Vol. 2. Preparation of stock for papermaking (1951). The first two of a series of volumes published under the ægis of the Joint Executive Committee on Vocational Education Representing the Pulp and Paper Industry of the United States and Canada.
J. P. *Casey,* Pulp and Paper (Vols. 1 and 2, 1952). An exhaustive compilation dealing with the chemistry and chemical technology of pulp and paper.

4.9. Nuclear Chemistry.

G. *Hevesy*, **Radioactive Indicators** (1948), gives a well-documented account of radioactive tracer techniques up to the date of publication.

Progress in Nuclear Energy Series (Vols. 1 and 2 are physical in content).

Vol. 3. *F. R. Bruce, J. M. Fletcher, H. H. Hyman and J. J. Katz*, Process chemistry.

Vol. 4. *R. Hurst and S. McLain*, Technology, materials and metallurgy.

Vol. 5. *J. C. Bugher, J. Coursaget and J. F. Loutit*, Biological science and medicine.

Vol. 6. *J. Guéron, J. A. Lane, I. R. Maxwell and J. Menke*, Economics of nuclear power.

J. G. Beckerley (Editor), **Geneva Series of Volumes on Nuclear Science**, dealing with peaceful applications.

Vol. 1. Safety aspects of nuclear reactors.

Vol. 2. Power reactors.

Vol. 3. Research reactors.

Vol. 4. Nuclear fuels.

Vol. 5. Atomic raw materials.

Vol. 6. Applications of nuclear radiation in food and agriculture.

CHAPTER V

REFERENCE WORKS ON MEDICINAL CHEMICALS

SECTIONS 4·1 to 4·8 contain only a few references to the subject matter of this chapter, since they are largely concerned with generalities. This section, on the other hand, is given as an example of the many points which have to be considered in searching a borderland subject. It will, of course, be realized that there are many such subjects, and only a single, typical field can be discussed in detail.

Medicinal chemicals can be considered from four main viewpoints:-

1. The methods used in their synthesis or extraction.
2. The analytical methods used for their examination for control purposes.
3. The mechanism underlying their biological action (particularly the relation of chemical constitution to physiological activity).
4. Their utilization in medicine.

and it might be thought that the literature of the subjects would be similarly sharply divided; unfortunately, this is not the case and, moreover, it is scarcely possible without an intelligent appreciation of how a drug works, and the field in which it is applied, to conduct research in the synthesis of new remedies. In other words, the four apparent main divisions of the subject shew such a degree of interpenetration that their separation, for purposes of literature searches is almost impossible.

5·1. **Methods of Synthesis and Extraction.**

Apart from communications to the journals, there are comparatively few books specially devoted to this aspect of the subject. Among the more important are:-

E. Fourneau, **Organic Medicaments and their Preparation** (1925). A selected, and comparatively small, group of drugs has been selected as representative of the various processes involved in the synthesis of medicinal chemicals, and these are described on a laboratory scale. A quarter of a century has elapsed since the book was written, but many of the processes are still in use.

M. Barrowcliff and F. H. Carr, **Organic Medicinal Chemicals** (1921). This book gives details of the industrial production of a large number of drugs by synthesis. The date of publication implies, of course, that only the older substances are dealt with.

S. Fränkel, **Die Arzneimittelsynthese** (6th Edition, 1927). This is a more elaborate treatise than the two previous citations, and gives data on a vast number of substances many of which have never attained practical usage for any considerable period.

K. H. Slotta, **Grundriss der modernen Arzneistoff-synthese** (1931). This is a summary of the production methods used for the more common medicinal chemicals. It gives an historical account of the various production methods and an outline of the preferred synthesis.

P. May and G. M. Dyson, **Chemistry of Synthetic Drugs** (4th Edition, 1939). This work is a survey of the synthetic organic substances used in medicine and of the methods of their preparation. The 5th Edition is now in the Press.

E. Waser, **Synthese der organischen Arzneimittel** (1928). This work deals exclusively with preparative methods.

N. Evers, **The Chemistry of Drugs** (2nd Edition, 1938). This volume describes not only synthetic, but also naturally occurring, drugs, mainly from the standpoint of pure chemistry.

H. P. Kaufmann, **Arzneimittel-synthese** (1953). A detailed survey of the chemistry of synthetic drugs.

C. M. Suter (Editor), **Medicinal Chemistry** (Vol. 1, 1951). A series of volumes dealing with synthetic drugs (synthesis and testing). Vol. 1 discusses antithyroid compounds, antispasmodics, plant antibiotics, benzoates as local anæsthetics and analgesics.

A. Burger, **Medicinal Chemistry** (2 Vols., 1951). A survey of chemical data on the synthesis and performance of synthetic drugs.

R. Fleck, **Synthetic Drugs** (1955). A somewhat abbreviated account of the main commercially important synthetic drugs.

Martindale's **Extra Pharmacopœia** (2 Vols., 23rd Edition, 1955) is a useful means of locating the lesser known medicinal compounds.

H. Gilman (Editor), **Organic Chemistry; an Advanced Treatise.** Vol. III (1953) has two very good survey chapters on chemotherapy and antibiotics.

Besides such works as are cited above, there are numerous monographs and specialized treatises on a single drug, or group of associated drugs, which deal with the chemistry of the subject; in some cases the works are biochemical in nature. Examples are:-

J. E. Jorpes, **Heparin** (1939).

D. W. Hill and F. O. Howitt, **Insulin** (1938).

E. Northey, **Sulphonamides and related Compounds** (1948).

T. Henry, **The Plant Alkaloids** (3rd Edition, 1939).

A. Stoll, **The Cardiac Glycosides** (1937).

G. T. Morgan, **Organic Compounds of Arsenic and Antimony** (1918).

G. W. Raiziss and J. L. Gavron, **Organic Arsenical Compounds** (1923).

F. C. Whitmore, **Organic Compounds of Mercury** (1921).

W. G. Christiansen, **Organic Derivatives of Antimony** (1924).

E. C. Kendall, **Thyroxine** (1929).

W. F. v. Oettingen, **Therapeutic Agents of the Quinoline Group** (1933).

H. T. Clarke, J. R. Johnson and R. Robinson, **The Chemistry of Penicillin** (1949). This work gives a detailed account of the work done by an international research group on the production, structure and synthesis of penicillin.

Such works are valuable sources of data and can conveniently form the starting point of searches in their several fields. In addition, the **Annual Reports of the Chemical Society** and those of the **Society of Chemical Industry,** should be consulted. A source which is sometimes overlooked is the **Comptes Rendus** of the various conferences and congresses of the *International Union of Pure and Applied Chemistry.* For example, the **Comptes Rendus** of the 1925 conference contains an invaluable paper by *Fourneau* – 'Les relations entre la constitution chimique de corps et leur action therapeutique.'

Reference should also be made to the fact that published books are abstracted by title in **Chemical Abstracts** and a list can be compiled quite rapidly from the Decennial and Annual Indexes.

The Merck Index (7th Edition, 1950) is a valuable general information book on drugs of all kinds. The information is arranged in dictionary form.

5.2. Analytical Methods.

Analytical methods for control and examination of medicinal chemicals are seldom alone the subject of treatises; there are many works on the analysis of foods and drugs (largely because in most countries the statutory control of both foods and drugs is under the same authority and Acts). The Pharmacopœias of various countries cite their methods of examination of accepted remedies, but an abstract and journal search is almost always necessary to find the bulk of the data in the field.

5.3. The Underlying Mechanism.

The mechanism underlying the mode of action of drugs is only just beginning to be understood, and, as yet, the correlation between the physical structure of the molecule and its biological action is merely tentative. Such works as those cited below deal either with the principles underlying drug action, or the relation of constitution to activity.

W. A. Sexton, **Chemical Constitution and Biological Activity** (2nd Edition, 1952). A volume of wide application, dealing with the fundamental correlation of structure and biological activity in all spheres.

T. S. and E. Work, **The Basis of Chemotherapy** (1948). The term 'chemotherapy' is used here in its modern sense of the action of chemical substances in combating infections of the animal system. This is one of the few books giving an ordered account of drug action. The volume contains a copious and most useful (although not complete) bibliography of the subject.

A. J. Clark, **The Mode of Action of Drugs on Cells** (1933). This work is somewhat similar to the former, but has a more limited scope.

G. M. Dyson, **Chemistry of Chemotherapy** (1928). This and the next work discuss in detail the inter-relation of physiological action and chemical constitution.

G. Barger, **Organic Chemistry in Biology and Medicine** (1930).
R. N. Chopra and A. C. Chandler, **Anthelmintics and their Uses** (1928).
C. H. Browning, **Studies in Antiseptics** (1918).
G. M. Findlay, **Recent Advances in Chemotherapy** (1930).
G. Hanzlik, **Actions and Uses of Salicylates** (1926).

5.4. Utilization of Drugs.

There is no lack of treatises on this subject, written mainly, of course, from the medical standpoint. Of the many such that have an interest for the chemist operating in the field of synthetic drugs, the following may be cited:-

A. J. Clark, **Applied Pharmacology** (6th Edition, 1937).
P. Ehrlich and E. Hata, **Chemotherapy der Spirillosen** (1910).
V. Fischl and H. Schlossberger, **Handbuch der Chemotherapie** (1934).
L. Rogers, **Recent Advances in Tropical Medicine** (2nd Edition, 1929).
E. Winterstein, **Die Narcose** (1926).
T. Sollmann, **Manual of Pharmacology** (6th Edition, 1943).
H. Balme, **The Relief of Pain** (1936).
J. Adriani, **The Pharmacology of Anæsthetic Drugs** (1941).
L. Goodman and A. Gilman, **The Pharmacological Basis of Therapeutics** (1941). This volume has exceptionally good bibliographies of each of the many topics discussed.
L. Meyler, **Side Effects of Drugs** (1952).

This rather more detailed survey of the treatises on a limited aspect of applied organic chemistry is by no means a complete bibliography, it charts, so to speak, only the main mountains and peaks in a widespread range.

CHAPTER VI

MAKING A SEARCH OF THE LITERATURE

IT is first requisite to determine precisely the scope of the search; if the physical properties or method of preparation of an organic compound be required, it may be wasted effort to make a full search of the literature. On the other hand, the time consumed on a library search is considerable and if the purpose in hand and the possibilities of future work warrant it, a complete search is often the best course; a search of half the literature often takes little less time than a full search.

It may be added, also, that there are obvious common-sense techniques for avoiding a search of the literature! – and a research worker should weigh up carefully whether (in the event, for example, of his desiring to know if X is soluble in Y) a few minutes in the laboratory may not avoid the expenditure of several hours in the library.

Searching techniques differ in various branches of chemistry and for convenience the art of searching will be subdivided as follows:-

6·1 Organic Chemistry.
6·2 Inorganic Chemistry.
6·3 Physical Chemistry.
6·4 Biological Chemistry.
6·5 Industrial Chemistry.

6·1. Organic Chemistry.

If a melting point, or a method of preparation, is all that it is desired to know of a fairly well-known compound, a reference to **Heilbron's Dictionary**, and to the volumes of **Organic Syntheses** is worth while as an opening gambit, and may prove a short cut to the desired bit of information. Frequently, however, it is necessary to go to the trouble of making a full search which, speaking bibliographically, should be as complete as possible.

Let it, therefore, be assumed that the search is to ascertain all that is known about a given structure, taking as an example 4,4'-dimethoxydibenzyl:-

$$CH_3O\langle\rangle CH_2CH_2\langle\rangle OCH_3 \qquad C_{16}H_{18}O_2$$

In searching, one necessary prerequisite is a certain agility in nomenclature, as it would appear that this compound may be called 'p,p'-dimethoxydiphenyl ethane', or a 'dimethoxydihydrostilbene', or even 'dianisyl'. If in doubt it is best to make a search under the molecular formula $C_{16}H_{18}O_2$. The first reference work to be consulted must be **Beilstein**; reference to the index will shew that data on this compound is available in the main volume VI and in its first and second supplements. The entries read:-

Beilstein, Vol. H VI, p. 1000.

4,4'-Dimethoxy-dibenzyl, α.β-Bis-[4-methoxy-phenyl]-äthan. $C_{16}H_{18}O_2 = [-CH_2 \cdot C_6H_4 \cdot O \cdot CH_3]_2$. B. Aus bis-[4-methoxy-benzyl]-disulfid beim Erhitzen mit Kupferpulver für sich oder in Xylollösung (*Manchot, Zahn,* A.345,329). Wurde bei der Aufarbeitung erhalten, als man Anisylchlorid (S.403), Magnesium und wenig Jod in Äther erwärmte und Cotarnincyanid eintrug (*Freund, Reitz,* B.39,2235). - Krystalle (aus Alkohol). F:125° (*F.,R*). Sehr leicht löslich in kaltem Aceton und Chloroform, leicht in siedendem Alkohol und Benzol (*M.,Z*). - Die Lösung in konz. Schwefelsäure gibt mit FeCl$_3$ Rotfärbung (*M.,Z*). Gibt met Brom in Chloroform ein Dibromderivat (S.1001, Z.3 v.u.) (*M.,Z*).

Beilstein, Vol. E I. 6 p. 490.

4,4'-Dimethoxy-dibenzyl $C_{16}H_{18}O_2 = CH_3 \cdot O \cdot C_6H_4 \cdot CH_2 \cdot CH_2 \cdot C_6H_4 \cdot O \cdot CH_3$ (S.1000). B. Bei der Umsetzung von 4-Methoxy-benzylbromid mit Alkyl- und Arylmagnesiumhalogeniden *Späth,* M.34,2002). - Krystalle (aus Alkohol), F:126-127°.

Beilstein, Vol. E II. 6 p. 967.

4,4'-Dimethoxy-dibenzyl, 1.2-Bis-[4-methoxy-phenyl]-äthan, Dianisyl $C_{16}H_{18}O_2 = CH_3 \cdot O \cdot C_6H_4 \cdot CH_2 \cdot CH_2 \cdot C_6H_4 \cdot O \cdot CH_3$ (H.

1000; E I 490). B. Durch Hydrierung von 4,4'-Di-
methoxy-stilben in Gegenwart von Platinoxyd in Essiges-
ter bei 60° (*Buck, Jenkins,* Am. Soc. 51,2166) oder von
4,4'-Dimethoxy-tolan in Gegenwart von Palladium-Barium-
sulfat in reinem Dioxan (*Schlenk, Bergmann,* A.463,124).
- Krystalle (aus Propylalkohol) F.123° (*Sch.,Be.*); 125°
(*Buck,* J.). Löslich in Eisessig (*Sch.,Be.*). - Färbt
konz. Schwefelsäure braunstichig rot (*Sch.,Be.*).

Bearing in mind that **Beilstein** and its two supplements
cover the periods (a) up to 1909, (b) 1910-1919, (c) 1920-1929,
it is clear that a search must now be made for the work done in
the last two decades. This is fairly easy for the decennial
indexes of **Chemical Abstracts** will give the periods 1927-1936
and 1937-1946. Thereafter the individual annual indexes must
be used. The entries found therein are:-

1927-1936	*Bibenzyl, p,p'-dimethoxy	24:847[4]
1937-1946	Bibenzyl, 4,4'-dimethoxy	34:2356[5]
	... ...	35:7948[7]
	... ...	38:73[4]
1947-1948	Nil	
1949	Bibenzyl, 4,4'-dimethoxy	43:191g
1950-1951	Nil	
1952	Bibenzyldimethoxy	46:4510d
1953	Nil	
1954	Bibenzyl, 4,4'-dimethoxy	48:3317c, 7575a.

On examination these shew the following data:-

24:847[4]. This proves to be the paper of *Buck and Jenkins*
(J.A.C.S. 1929,51,2163) already cited in **Beilstein.** Since
this was published in 1929 it might have been thought that it
could have been eliminated from the list of references
without inspection; this is inadvisable, as a bibliographical
check at the borderline between **Beilstein** and **Abstract**
indexes is valuable.

34:2356[5]. *E.M. Richardson and E. Emmet Reid,* J.A.C.S. 1940,
62,413. It is indicated that the compound was obtained in

---

* It will be noted that the A.C.S. use 'bibenzyl', not 'dibenzyl'.
There is, however, a cross reference in the index between the
two forms.

72% yield by catalytic reduction of the corresponding stilbene with PtO_2 (and, presumably, with hydrogen. Ed.). m. 125·5°-127°.

35:7948[7]. *Antonio Sosa*, Ann. Chim. 1940,**14**,5. Attempted condensation of $MeOC_6H_4CH_2Cl$ with EtCHO produces p,p'-dimethoxydibenzyl, m. 128·5° (block) and 130°.

38:74[4]. *Richard Baltzly and J. S. Buck*, J.A.C.S. 1943,**65**,1984. The compound was obtained by reduction of anisoin ($CH_3O·C_6H_4·CO·CHOH·C_6H_4·OCH_3$) with Pd and hydrogen.

43:191g. *E. C. Kleiderer and E. C. Kornfeld*, J. Org. Chem. 1948,**13**,455. The compound was obtained by reducing desoxyanisoin with Raney nickel in *cyclo*hexanol suspension; yield, 80%.

46:4510d. *A. T. Carpenter and R. F. Hunter*, J. Appl. Chem. 1951,**1**,217-26. In this abstract the compound is called 1,2-*bis*(p-methoxyphenyl)ethane, and the abstract states that the compound was prepared by a modification of the Clemmensen reduction of anisole; it is clear, of course, that no reduction of anisole could possibly give the required compound and here a reference to the original literature becomes essential. The original journal shews that the abstractor has written 'anisole' for 'anisil' so that diketone $MeOC_6H_4COCOC_6H_4OMe$ is the starting point for this synthesis. (Incidentally, these authors call the compound 1:2-di-(p-methoxyphenyl)ethane, so that we have here an interesting instance where three different names are used for the same substance – in the original, in the abstract and in the abstract index). The m. after recrystallization from methanol is given as 125°C., but the authors recognized that their product was somewhat impure.

The compound was also prepared by these workers in small yield by the action of anhydrous ferric chloride on the Grignard reagent from mixed o- and p-chloromethylanisole.

48:3317c. *R. C. Fuson and H. O. House*, J.A.C.S. 1953,**75**, 1325-7. These workers obtained a 37% yield of the compound by direct methylation of 1,2-*bis*(p-hydroxyphenyl)ethane with Me_2SO_4 and alkali; they give m. 125·5-126·5°C. with infra-red absorption bands at 1610, 1582, 1508, 1244 1052 and 833 cm.[-1]

48:7575a. *G. R. Yohe, D. R. Hill, J. E. Dunbar and F. M.*

Scheidt, J.A.C.S. 1953,**75**,2688-93. The compound was prepared by the reduction of anisoin by the Clemmensen-Martin method: the yield was very low (7%). No m.p. is given in the abstract, but the original paper gives 125·5-7°C.

It is now possible to draw up a summary of these data. The manner in which a summary is made is largely a matter of convenience and preference. The form used in the author's laboratory is shewn on pp. 84 and 85.

It may occur to the reader to ask why this particular example was chosen. The answer is that an example must satisfy all the following requirements:-

1. It must have references in **Beilstein** and in both supplements.
2. It should have references distributed throughout **Chemical Abstracts.**
3. There should not be too many references.
4. The compound should have a definite structural formula.
5. There should be some nomenclature variations associated with the structure, which illustrate different national usages and historical change.
6. If possible, there should be an odd reference in **Zentralblatt** not mentioned elsewhere, and a few literature 'mistakes'.

It should be emphasized that the material set out on pp. 78-82 is the minimum that has to be done in making a search. From the documentation angle, there are at least two weak spots in the work so far; first, mainly 'secondary' sources have been used, and second, no cross-check has been made. The term 'secondary' is used to differentiate compendia and abstracts from 'primary' or original communications. It will be clear that the certainty with which a searcher has obtained references to all original papers depends on three main factors:-

1. The fidelity with which the abstractor or compiler has transferred the matter from the primary to the secondary source, *i.e.* **Beilstein** or **Abstracts.**
2. The skill with which the indexer of the secondary source has provided in his indexes a reference to every mention of the substances for which the search is being made.

3. The thoroughness with which the searcher has done his task.

It is seldom that perfection is attained in all three sections at any given time; if each stage (abstract cover, indexing, searching) is 90% efficient, the overall efficiency will be 0.9^3 or 73.0%; this implies that three out of four original mentions will be obtained by the searcher using the technique so far described.

To improve this efficiency figure, a cross-check can be applied by making a parallel search in **British Abstracts** and in the quinquennial indexes of **Chemisches Zentralblatt**; in the latter case, a formula-index search being essential since the journal does not prepare an index of systematic names. Most entries will refer to the same papers as those cited by **Beilstein** and **Chemical Abstracts**, but here and there a new reference will turn up, e.g.

Chemisches Zentralblatt, 31,[1], 2044.
   H. Gilman and E. A. Zoellner, Bull. Soc. Chim. 1931,[4],49,7.
   Reference is made to the formation of 4,4'-dimethoxydibenzyl in a *Grignard* reaction.

How was it that this was overlooked in the first search? Examination shews that **Chemical Abstracts** has duly abstracted the paper (C.A. 1931,25,2126) and has mentioned the compound, but that it has been missed from the decennial index; hence, although present, it cannot answer to its name.

This shews the value of cross-checking, and it must in no sense be taken as a criticism of the manner in which **Chemical Abstracts** is indexed. It is merely one example of that imperfection of human endeavour which is encountered in any gigantic task, such as that which confronts the abstractors of chemical literature.

Can anything more now be done? This depends on the purpose in hand, and the degree of perfection desired. If a new research project is being planned, it would be essential to read at least the more important, if not all, of the original communications to which the abstracts refer. This is not just a means of checking the abstracts; reading the papers *in extenso* will confer the following benefits:-

1. The acquisition of a 'mental background' of the subject,

2616:22.2.789　　　　　　B6,G,8.C2.Q,4,12C

1,2-bis-[4-Methoxyphenyl]ethane.

4,4'-Dimethoxy dibenzyl　or　Bibenzyl,4,4'-dimethoxy-

1:2-Di-(p-methoxyphenyl)ethane.

	C H O	79.3　7.4　13.2%
		M.W. 242

CH₃O〈benzene〉CH₂CH₂〈benzene〉

m.p.	ref.	Infrared Lines
125°	2,5	835
126–127°	3	1052
123°	4	1244
125.5–127°	7,12	1508
125.5°	8	1582
125.5–126.5°	11	1610 cm⁻¹

Physical Properties. Xtallises in. alcohol easily; sol. in cold acetone, CHCl₃, + hot C₆H₆.①

Preparation. By reduction of 4,4'-dimethoxystilbene with H₂+Pt oxide in EtOH at 60°⑤; 72% yield⑥; by H₂+Pd/BaSO₄ in pure dioxan on 4,4'-dimethoxystilbene④; from anisyl chloride with Mg + trace I₂ in ether② or by action of CH₃CHO③ from anisyl bromide + Grignard reagents③④ by heating bis-(4-methoxybenzyl) disulphides with Cu powder② reducing desoxyanisoin with Raney Ni in cyclohexanol; 80% yd.⑥ reducing anisil⑫; anisoin⑫ or by writer then of the di-OH compound with H₂SO₄ + alkali.①

Properties. Red colour in conc. H_2SO_4 + $FeCl_3$ (1/4). with Br/$CHCl_3$
gives dibromo compound ①

Bibliographe.

1. Manchot, Zahn, Ann., 1906, 345, 329.
2. Freund, Reitz, Ber., 1906, 39, 2235.
3. Späth, Monats., 1913, 34, 2002.
4. Schlenk, Bergmann, Ann., 1928, 463, 124.
5. Buck, Jenkins, JACS, 1929, 51, 2166.
6. Gilman, Zoellner, Bull. Soc. Chim., 1931, [4]49, 17.
7. Richardson & Reid, JACS, 1940, 62, 443.
8. Sosa, Ann. Chim., 1940, 14, 5.
9. Kleiderer & Kornfeld, J. Org. Chem., 1948, 13, 455.
10. Carpenter & Hunter, J. Appl. Chem., 1951, 1, 217-26
11. Fuson & House, JACS, 1953, 75, 1325.
12. Yohe, Hill, Dunbar & Schädt, JACS, 1953, 75, 2688.

B. H6. 1000
B. H6. 1000
B. EII 6. 490
B. EIII 6. 967
B. EIII 6. 967
Z. 31(1, 2044
CA. 34: 2356[5]
CA. 35: 7498[7]
CA. 43: 1919
CA. 46: 4510d
CA. 48: 3317c
CA. 48: 7575a

a necessary preliminary to research.

2. The compilation of a valuable series of back-references from the original papers to other communications (not always noted in the abstracts) and an occasional 'find', thereby, in the shape of an otherwise unrecorded paper.

3. Information of a more detailed kind than can, of necessity, be included in abstracts.

It is for the reasons set out above that chemists must do a good proportion of their own searching, and not have it all done for them by library service. On the other hand, in large industrial organizations where the subjects of individual research change more frequently, the library service is of great value; but with the proviso that it is done by a chemist-librarian. Chemical commonsense is of the utmost value in making a thorough search for subject-matter, and there are certain little tricks that only a chemically trained person can know; such, for example, as the awareness that tucked away under the entry 'Benzoic acids, halogenated, dissociation constants of', may be data on 4-fluorobenzoic acid, which is not entered under 'Benzoic acid, 4-fluoro-. The thought should always be kept in mind during a search, that an index will only tell us just what we ask it, and imagination must be brought into play to think out possible alternative ways in which the essential questions may be put, or headings under which the vital information may have been entered.

Entry to the abstract literature may have been made through the subject index; if so, a valuable check may be arrived at by consulting the formula indexes, a task made easier by the publication of a collective formula index to Vols. 14-40 (1920-1946) of **Chemical Abstracts.** In many cases, where an unknown substance is being identified the formula indexes must be consulted to ascertain (a) if substances of the molecular formula are known, and (b) if so, whether any of the known structures shew points of similarity with the new compound.

Where, as in patent litigation, it is essential to make as complete a search as possible, it may be found useful to search under the names of authors known to have worked in the field, using, of course, the annual and cumulative author indexes.

Monographs and reviews are often good sources of that general information from which a good background knowledge of a subject can be acquired. Thus, to take a random example, from **Chemical Reviews,** consider the review on 'The Chemistry of the Pyrrocolines and the Octahydropyrrocolines'. This valuable paper contains material brought together by expert workers and its sources are cited as a series of 89 references. The unwary might be excused for assuming this to be the complete literature of the subject. Even so, a careful search of the indexes reveals that a paper by Ochiai, Tsuda and Yoko-maga (Ber. 68B, 2291) on the expansion of the octohydropyrroco-line ring is not cited.* There may be other omissions, and workers should not take the bibliographical completeness of a monograph for granted, unless this quality is specifically claimed by the authors.

As the searching of organic chemical literature is so important a feature of research in this field, a second example is given in **Appendix II.**

6.2. Inorganic Chemistry.

Here the mode of searching is not so stereotyped as in the organic field. For one thing, inorganic chemistry is more deeply rooted in antiquity, and whereas a fairly complete documentation of an organic compound can be carried out with **Beilstein** and the abstracts, this cannot so easily be accomplished for inorganic compounds that have been known for centuries.

If a full search is required, a good starting point is often to be found in **Gmelin**; the efficacy of such a procedure depends entirely on the date of the latest volume issued on the subject in question. Thus, on antimony the cover is excellent, volumes on this element having been issued in 1949; but if no new volume or supplement has appeared since the 8th edition (1921 onwards) the abstracts must be searched for the desired information. The treatises of **Abegg** and **Auerbach,** and of **Mellor,** are comprehensive and valuable source-books. The former is critical and the latter more comprehensive, but largely non-critical: both are, unfortunately, ageing, which necessitates a lengthy search through the abstracts, especially in the case of the elements of low atomic number. In this connexion, it should be remembered that **Chemical Abstracts**

---

* This is not a criticism of the authors' work; they probably had good and sufficient reasons for not including the paper.

enters the molecular formula of inorganic compounds in its formula indexes.

It is one peculiarity of inorganic chemistry that searches are less frequently made for the literature of individual substances, than for more general topics, such as Corrosion, General properties of Nitrides, Steel, etc., which are quite thoroughly entered in the abstract subject indexes.

6.3. Physical Chemistry.

It is far more difficult to search for a topic than for an individual compound. The latter has either been prepared or not; it is an entity sharply defined by its constitution and can be searched for in terms of its structure, which is unique. A topic, on the other hand, is less sharply defined and then only in terms of other concepts which may themselves be ill-defined. As an example consider searching for data on the Liesegang rings of colloid chemistry. The basic principle of localized concentrations in colloid systems underlying the ring formation may not necessarily, in an index, be entered under the heading of 'Liesegang'. Search must be made for information relating to the banded structure in minerals, in plant chemistry and a variety of other related topics, and it is much more a matter of skill and background knowledge on the part of the searcher to obtain a satisfactory survey in such a field, than to collect data on an individual compound.

There are numerous monographs on physical-chemical subjects which may be helpful, but the main recourse is to the abstract indexes, which must be searched under all likely headings. It is often helpful to read a summary of the topic in the **Annual Reports of The Chemical Society**, keeping an open eye for headings under which information might be indexed. A glance at the collective subject index of **Chemical Reviews**, and the similar index to Vols. 1-42 of the previously mentioned reports, is time well invested, as many suitable headings for a word-list may be found therein. It is again emphasized that there are no hard and fast rules in this kind of search, and its completeness will depend to a considerable extent on the skill of the searcher in detecting the right headings in the indexes, while there are rewards for those with wide background knowledge.

It may be appropriate to mention at this point that there are certain questions which it is well-nigh impossible to answer by a literature search. One is concerned with the literature of a substance largely used in the capacity of a reagent or solvent, such, for example, as phosgene, $COCl_2$. Where the main purport of a communication is the chemical or physical properties of phosgene, that substance will undoubtedly be mentioned in the title and in the index, but if it has been used casually to prepare a urea, in a synthesis where the urea is an intermediate or ancillary substance, it is unlikely that it will be indexed. The same is true of the usage of, say, diethyl carbonate as a solvent in a pyrimidine synthesis. There is also no simple method for searching the literature for substances with a combination of structural features, such, for example, as all ring compounds with hetero-sulphur and carboxyl groups.

6·4. Biological Chemistry.

The standard compendia of organic chemistry, such as **Beilstein,** do not give data on the physiological properties of the substances they describe. Hence, a search for physiological data on organic compounds is more difficult than for purely chemical data. It must be added that certain physiological data is given in **Elsevier's Encyclopædia,** but this work is not yet sufficiently advanced in compilation and publication to serve as a generally convenient source-book. One mitigating factor is that physiological data prior to 1900 are of little importance, except for historical purposes, so that it is seldom necessary to continue a search back into the 19th century. The larger works mentioned in section 5·1 are convenient starting points, and reinforced by the abstract indexes make a good basis for a search.

6·5. Industrial Chemistry.

If a general outline is wanted of an industrial process, **Ullmann** is a good starting point and the indexes of **Ind. Eng. Chem.** and of the **Industrial Chemist,** will help to follow up the subject. A more detailed search will have to be made in the **Patent** literature, **Chemical Abstracts,** and the usual cross-check with **British Abstracts** and **Zentralblatt.** It will be found that the abstracts on many technical contributions to trade journals are shorter than those of the more academic papers. This necessitates more frequent consultation of originals. The policy of abstract journals is to publish abstracts of new matter, but not to deal more than cursorily with summaries and reviews. This policy, correct and judicious as it must be admitted to be, has the effect of excluding from abstracts more than a titular reference to many contributions which would serve as excellent introductions to the study of an industrial problem. These must, therefore, be consulted in the original form. Nevertheless, the guiding principles of searching are similar to those in other sections; considerable use is also made of the chemical engineering journals.

6.6. Some General Remarks.

The following hints are given to students to whom literature searching comes as a new part of their work:-

1. Never commence any research project without making as thorough a search as can be done with the facilities available. Even if you have to start your enquiries with a text-book, note its date of publication and search the abstracts for subsequent work. There are few disappointments so keen, in science, as the discovery that the work you have just laboriously completed, had been done by others and published before you began it.

2. Do your own searching, if possible; do not rely on others if you can in any way avoid doing so.

3. When searching **Beilstein**, or **Abstracts**, or any of the similar volumes, make a complete list of references (in chronological order) before commencing to look at the entries. This is more a matter of psychology than of chemistry, since it negatives the tendency to leave an index survey uncompleted after having once obtained a substantial bulk of information following a partial survey.

4. Make a word-list of all likely index headings before commencing a search; add to this any that may become evident during searching.

5. Keep a special set of notebooks for literature searches, and make an ink record of each search. Scraps of paper are proverbially fugitive, and the repetition of a search is exasperating.

Finally, make a habit of reading systematically about and around any subject in which you are engaged. **Nature** each week, **Chemical Abstracts** each fortnight, and the monthly national journals appropriate to your section of the subject, will give you a background; it is not a matter of remembering the whole of this reading but of preparing the mind, which thereby acquires a 'state of awareness' which sensitizes it to the impact of experimental observations.

6·7. Libraries.

Some notes on the general library facilities in England may be of help to the beginner. As a piece of general advice to the student one cannot do better than to recommend him to get to know thoroughly both the library and the librarian; the latter is, usually, only too eager to ensure the full use of the volumes on his shelves; he will always take the greatest pains to solve any difficulty that arises and to spend his time ungrudgingly to this end; it is, therefore, only courteous and considerate to make every effort ourselves to find the required information before burdening the librarian with our difficulties.

Library Facilities in England.

Apart from the libraries of the Universities and larger Technical Colleges there exists a number of central libraries and facilities with which every student should become familiar.

1. **The Library of The Chemical Society** is one of the finest collections of chemical books in the country and is available for personal consultation or by loan to members of the Society itself and to those of several associated societies. Enquiries are to be addressed to The Librarian, The Chemical Society, Burlington House, Piccadilly, London, W.1. (Telephone REGent 1675).

2. **The Library of the Science Museum** also has a full holding of chemical books and journals and students can, by permission, use the library during the normal hours of opening. If more than a casual visit is p lanned a ticket should be obtained from The Director, The Science Museum, South Kensington, London, S.W.7. Copies are available on loan of many publications. Copies of the library's lists of periodicals are useful investments showing all those available by consultation or on loan, and also those not loanable. The telephone number is KENsington 6371, Extn. 227.

Both The Chemical Society's and the Science Museum's

libraries have photocopying services which enable students to obtain copies for their own research or study of important articles.

3. **The Library of the Patent Office.** This contains one of the best collections of journals in pure and applied chemistry in London. It may be consulted by any member of the public on signing an attendance book. The library is almost entirely an 'open access' collection. Address: 25 Southampton Buildings, London, W.C.2.

4. **Aslib.** The Association of Special Libraries and Information Bureaux has done a great deal of important work for scientific (including chemical) literature. It publishes titles of theses submitted for higher degrees – a valuable source of detailed chemical information and performs innumerable services, too many to mention here. The Association will always assist a student in locating an obscure source, but it should be a point of honour with all workers to make a proper search in the ordinary library channels before enlisting the aid of Aslib, 4 Palace Gate, London, W.8.

5. **The Technical Information Service of the** D.S.I.R. (Charles House, 5-11 Regent St., London, S.W.1.) and the **National Central Library,** Malet Place, London, W.C.1 are organizations which the advanced student should enquire about. Information on most of these can be obtained from the following:-

The Library Service of Great Britain. University of London, Advisory Service for External Students. 1951. Gratis to external students.

British Sources of Reference and Information: A guide to societies, works of reference and libraries. T. Besterman. Aslib, 1947. 6s.

The Libraries of Greater London. L.M. Harrod. Bell & Sons, Ltd., 1951. 25s.

World List of Scientific Periodicals. Butterworths Scientific Publications, Ltd. Third edition, 1952. 252s.

Hand List of Short Titles of Current Periodicals in the Science Library. Sixth edition. H.M.S.O., 1950. 10s.

Brief Guide to the Research Activities of D.S.I.R. and the Research Associations. D.S.I.R., 1951. On request.

Government Scientific Organization in the Civilian Field.
Chapter VII.   Scientific and Technical Information Services.   H.M.S.O., 1951.   1s. 6d.
Scientific and Learned Societies of Great Britain.   Allen and Unwin (for the British Council), 1951.   30s.
The World of Learning.   4th edition.   Europa Publications, Ltd., 1952.   80s.

SOME OLD AND OBSOLETE JOURNALS

IT is, perhaps, not often that the ordinary worker is called upon to search minutely in the literature prior to 1875. Occasional references may be found to earlier work but, usually, this date (chosen, incidentally, because by that time the abstracts of *The Chemical Society* were well under way) marks the point beyond which it is unnecessary to go, except for historical purposes.

On the few occasions, however, when detailed early knowledge is essential, it must be remembered that much work done between 1775-1875 is housed in journals now obsolete. The most important of such are listed in the TABLE which forms the major part of this appendix. In addition, the following notes may be of assistance to beginners in this branch of searching.

1. **Multiple Publication.** In early times, investigators published the same account of their work, often word for word, in several different journals. Do not, therefore, be unduly disappointed on finding that an obscure Swedish paper, for example, by *Berzelius* is merely an old friend in another language.

2. **Anonymity.** Remember that there was a period when serious scientific papers could be published anonymously. To discover the authors of such papers is, in itself, a special field of bibliographical research, outside the scope of ordinary work.

3. **Mode of Reference.** It was a smaller and more personal chemical world a century ago, and most workers were known personally to one another; citations were frequently made, not to the title of a journal but to the name of its editor; thus 'Pogg.' refers to the **Annalen**

edited by *Poggendorf;* 'Schw.' refers to the Journal für die Chemie, edited by *Schweigger;* and we even find 'Brugn. G.' for the Giornale di fisica, chimica etc., edited by *Brugnatelli.* This implies an apparent change of title when the editor changes.

4. **Indexes.** Exhaustive indexes were not usual in the early days of chemical literature; a contents table and index of general topics is all that can be expected; cumulative indexes are equally rare.

SOME OBSOLETE CHEMICAL JOURNALS OF THE NINETEENTH CENTURY

No.	Title	Published from	Date	Vols.	Editor
1	Afhandlingar i Fysik, Kemi och Mineralogi.	Stockholm	1806-1818	6	Berzelius and Hisinger.
2	Allgemeine chemische Bibliothek des Neunzehnten Jahrhunderts.	Erfurt	Irreg. 1801-1805	5	Trommsdorff.
3	Allgemeine Journal der Chemie. *continued as:-*	Leipzig	1798-1803	10	Scherer.
	Neues allgemeine J.f. Chemie. *continued as:-*	Leipzig	1803-1806	8	Gehlen.
	Journal f. die Chemie, Physik &c. 2nd Series	Berlin Nurnberg	1806-1810 1811-1833	9 69	Gehlen. Schweigger.
	(This journal was merged in 1834 with others in J. Pr. Chem.).				
4	Almanach de la Chimie.	Rouen and Paris	1854-1861	8	H. du M.
5	Almanach fur Scheidekunstler und Apotheker. *continued as:-*	Weimar	1780-1802	23	Gottling.
	Taschenbuch fur S. and A. *continued as:-*	Weimar	1803-1819	17	Bucholz.
	Trommsdorff's Taschenbuch fur Chemiker und Pharmaceuten.	Jena	1820-1829	10	Trommsdorff.
	(Cumulative Index 1780-1803).				
6	American Chemical Journal.	Baltimore	1878-1913	50	Remsen *et al.*
7	American Laboratory.	Boston	1875	1	-
8	American Chemist.	New York	1870-1877	6+	Chandler.
9	Annali di Chimica.	Pavia	1790-1802	21	Brugnatelli.
	(Cumulative Index at Vol. 21).				

No.	Title	Place	Years	Vols.	Editor
10	Annali di fisica, chimica e matematiche.	Milano	1841-1847	28	Majocchi.
	continued as:- Annali di fisica, chimica e scienze affini.	Torino	1850-1851	6	Majocci and Selmi.
11	Annals of Chemical Medicine.	London	1880- ?	?	Thudicum.
12	Annals of Chemical Philosophy.	London	1828-1829	2	Maugham.
13	Annals of Chemistry and practical Pharmacy.	London	1843	1	—
14	Annals of Philosophy, 1st Series.	London	1813-1820	16	Thomson.
	Annals of Philosophy, 2nd Series. (Merged in Phil. Mag. in 1827).	London	1821-1826	12	Phillips.
15	Annuaire de Chimie.	Paris	1845-1851	7	Millon and Reisst.
16	Annuaire des Sciences chimiques.	Paris	1837	1	Berzelius.
17	Annual Reports of the Progress of Chemistry (English translation of the Jahresberichte).	London	1849-1855	7	Liebig *et al.*
18	Annuario delle scienzi chimiche farmaceutiche e medicolegal.	Mantova	1840-1841	1	—
	2nd Series	Mantova	1841-1849	9	Sembenini.
19	Archiv f. Gesammte Naturlehre. *continued as:-*	Nurnberg	1824-1830	18	Kastner.
20	Archiv f. Chemie und Meteorologie.	Nurnberg	1830-1835	9	Kastner.
21	Archiv f. die theoretische Chemie.	Jena	1800-1802	1	Scherer.
	Archiv f. die thierische Chemie.	Halle	1800-1801	1	Horkel.
22	Årsberattelse om Framstegen i Physik och Kemi till Kongl. Vet. Akad. etc., *continued as:-*	Stockholm	1821-1840	20	Berzelius.
	Årsberattelse om Framstegen i Kemi och Mineralogi till Kongl. Vet. Akad. etc., *continued with omission of* 'och Mineralogi'.	Stockholm	1841-1847	7	Berzelius.
		Stockholm	1847-1849	3	**Svanberg.**

No.	Title	Published from	Date	Vols.	Editor
23	Abhandlungen aller eigenthumlicher und Beobachtungen in der Chemie.	Leipzig	1786-1787	5	Crell.
24	Beitrage zur Chemie.	Wien	1781	1	Wasserberg.
25	Beitrage zur chemische Kentniss der Mineralkorper.	Berlin and Stettin	1795-1815	6	Klaproth.
26	Beitrage zur Erweiterung und Berichtigung der Chemie.	Erfurt	1799-1802	3	Bucholz.
27	Beitrage zur physiologischen und pathologischen Chemie. *continued as:-*	Berlin	1843-1844	1	Simon.
	Archiv. f. pharm. u. path. Chemie.*	Wien	1844-1854	8	Heller.
28	Berlinisches Jahrbuch der Pharmacie.	Berlin	1795-1840	43	Gehlen, Rose, Dobereiner *et al.*
29	Bibliothek der neuesten Physich-Chemischen Literatur. *continued as:-*	Berlin	1788-1795	4	Hermbstadt.
	Annalen der chemischen Literatur.	Berlin	1801-1802	1	v. Woolf.
30	Boston Journal of Chemistry. *continued as:-*	Boston	1866-1880	14	Nichols.
	Boston Journal of Chemistry and Popular Science. *continued as:-*	Boston	1881-1882	2	—
	Popular Science News and Boston Journal of Chemistry.	Boston	1884	?	—
31	Bulletin des sciences mathematiques, astronomiques, physiques et chimiques.	Paris	1824-1831	16	Saigey.

* Not to be confused with Arch. f. exptl. Path. u. Pharm, started in 1873.

No.	Title	Place	Dates	Vol.	Editor
32	Centralblatt f. Agricultur. Chemie.	Leipzig	1872-1885	24	Biedermann.
33	The Chemical Gazette.	London	1843-1859	17	Francis and Croft.
	continued as:-				
34	Chemical News.	London	1860-1932	145	Crookes.
35	Chemical Review.	London	1871-1884	14	—
	Chemical Review, and Journal for the spirit, vinegar and sugar Industry.	Chicago	1881	1	Siebel.
	continued as:-				
36	American Chemical Review etc.	Chicago	1882-1884	3	—
	Chemische Ackersmann.	Leipzig	1855-1875	21	Stockhardt.
37	Chemische Annalen fur die Freunde der Natur-lehre.	Helmstadt and Leipzig	1784-1803	40	Crell.
	and associated with:-				
	Beitrage zu den chemischen Annalen von L. Crell.	Helmstadt and Leipzig	1785-1799	6	Crell.
38	Chemische en phijsische oefeningen voor de beminnaars der schei- en naturkunde.	Amsterdam and Leyden	1788	3	Kastelyn.
39	Chemische Archiv.	Leipzig	1783-1784	2	Crell.
	continued as:-				
	Neues Chemische Archiv.	Leipzig	1784-1791	8	Crell.
	continued as:-				
	Neuestes Chemische Archiv.	Weimar	1798	1	Crell.
40	Chemische Journal fur die Freunde der Natur-lehre.	Lemgo	1778-1781	6	Crell.
	continued as:-				
	Entdechungen (Die neuestes) in der Chemie.	Leipzig	1781-1786	13	Crell.
41	Chemisch-Technischen Mittheilungen der neuesten Zeit.	Berlin	1846-1883	33	Elsner.
42	Chemische-Technisches Rept.	Berlin	1862-1882	21	Jacobson.

No.	Title	Published from	Date	Vols.	Editor
43	Chemist (The), 1st Series.	London	1824-1825	2	—
	2nd Series.	London	1840-1845	6	C. and J. Watt.
	3rd Series.	London	1846-1848	1	Newton.
	4th Series.	London	1849-1853	4	C. and J. Watt.
	5th Series.	London	1854-1858	5	C. and J. Watt.
44	Chemists Journal (The).	London	1880-1882	6	—
45	Chimiste (Le), Agricultural.	Bruxelles	1865-1869	5	Berge.
46	Chimiste (Le), Distillers.	Paris	1859-1860	2	Simon.
47	Crell's Chemical Journal (Translation of No. 37 but with additions).	London	1791-1793	3	—
48	Edinburgh Journal of Science (Merged in Phil. Mag., 1832).	Edinburgh	1824-1832	16	Brewster et al.
49	Gazzetta eclettica di chimica technologia.	Verona	1833-1834	2	Sembenini.
50	Gazzetta eclettica di chimica pharmacia.	Verona	1831-1839	7	Sembenini.
51	Giornale de Farmacia, chimica. continued as:-	Milano	1824-1834	19	Cattanco.
	Bibliothek di Farmacia. continued as:-	Milano	1834-1845	23	Cattanco.
	Annali di chimica applicata (continued into 20th century).	Milano	1845+	71+	Pelli et al.
52	Giornale di chimica, fisica e storia naturale. continued with addition of 'medicina ed arte'.	Pavia	1808-1817	10	Brugnatelli.
		Pavia	1818-1827	10	Brugnatelli.
53	Introduction aux observations sur la physique, sur l'histoire naturelle et sur les arts. continued as:-	Paris	1771-1772 (A second issue 1777)	18	Rozier.
	Observations et mémoires etc. continued as:-	Paris	1773	1	Rozier.

		Place	Date	Vols.	Rozier et al.
	Observations sur la physique etc.	Paris	1778-1794	42 (Nos. 2-43)	la Metherie et al.
	continued as:-				
	Journal de physique, de chimie etc.	Paris	1794-1822	53	-
54	Jahrbuch der erfindungen und Fortschritte auf den d. gebieten der Physik und Chemie.	Leipzig	1865-1884	20	
55	Jahresberichte der Agriculturchem.	Berlin	1875	2	Detmer.
56	Jahresberichte uber die Fortshcritte der physichen Wissenschaften.	Tubingen	1822-1841	20	Berzelius.
	continued as:-				
	J. u. d. F. d. Chemie u. Mineralogie (No. 22, trans. fr. Swedish).	Tubingen	1842-1851	10	Berzelius.
57	Journal de chimie medicale, de pharmacie et de toxicologie.	Paris	1825-1834	10	-
	continued as:- 2nd Series.	Paris	1835-1844	10	
	3rd Series.	Paris	1845-1854	10	
	4th Series.	Paris	1855-1864	10	
	5th Series.	Paris	1865-1876	12	
	(Minor changes in title between Series; merged in Ref. Pharm., 1876).				
58	Journal f. Physik u. physikalisches Chemie des Auslandes.	Berlin	1851	3	Kronig.
59	Journal für technische und ökonomische Chemie.	Leipzig	1828-1833	18	Erdmann.
60	Journal of Applied Chemistry.	New York	1866-1875	10	
61	Journal of natural philosophy, chemistry and the arts.	London	1797-1801	5	Nicholson.
62	Kleine physikalische-chemische Abhandlungen.	London	1802-1813	36	Nicholson.
	2nd Series	Leipzig	1858	8	Westrumb.

No.	Title	Published from	Date	Vols.	Editor
63	Kritische Zeitschrift für Chemie, Physik und Mathematik.	Erlangen	1858	1	Kekulé et al.
	2nd Series	Erlangen	1859	1	Erlenmeyer.
	continued as:- Zeitschrift für Chemie und Pharmacie.	Erlangen and Heidelberg	1860-1864	4	Beilstein and Fittig.
	continued as:- Zeitschrift für Chemie.	Göttingen	1865-1871	7	(As above).
64	Laboratorium (Das).	Weimar	1825-1840	44	-
65	Laboratory (The).	Boston	1874-1876	2	Babcock.
66	Laboratory (The).	London	1867	1	-
67	Magazin für die hohere Naturwissenschaft und Chemie.	Tubingen	1784-1787	2	-
68	Mechanic and Chemist.	London	1836-1842	8	-
69	Melanges physiques et chimiques tirés de Bulletin ... de St. Petersbourg.	St. Petersbourg	1854-1884+	12+	-
70	Memoirs of the Columbian Chemical Society.	Philadelphia	1813-1814	2	-
71	Naturhistorische und chemische technische Notizen.	Berlin	1854-1859	11	-
72	Nordische Blatter für Chemie.	Berlin	1860-1862	4	-
	2nd Series	Halle	1817	1	Scherer.
	continued as:- Allgemeine nordische Annalen der Chemie.	St. Petersbourg	1819-1822	7	Scherer.
	continued as:- Magazin f. d. neuesten Erfahrung (Merged with Annalen der Pharmacie, 1832).	Carlsruhe	1823-1831	36	Hanle and Geiger.

No.	Title	City	Years	Vols	Editor
73	Penny Mechanic and Chemist.	London	1836-1842	8	—
74	Pharmaceutical Times.	London	1847-1848	3	—
	continued as:-				
75	Chemical Times.	London	1848-1849	2	—
	Raccolta fisica-chimica Italiana.	Venezia	1846-1848	3	Zantedeschi.
	continued as:-				
76	Annali di fisica.	Padova	1849-1850	1	Zantedeschi.
	Repertoire de chimie et de physique etc.	Paris	1837-1839	6	—
77	Repertoire de Chimie pure et appliquée (Each Vol. is in two parts, A and B. It became Bull. Soc. Chim. in 1864).	Paris	1858-1863	5	—
78	Repertorium für die Pharmacie.	Nurnberg	1815-1834	50	Buchner.
	2nd Series.	Nurnberg	1835-1848	50	Buchner.
	3rd Series.	Nurnberg	1849-1851	10	Buchner.
	continued as:-				
79	Repertorium (Neues etc.).	Nurnberg	1852-1876	25	Buchner.
80	Repertorium für Chemie.	Nurnberg	1790-1796	7	Elvert.
81	Repertorium für organischen Chemie.	Zurich	1841-1843	3	Löwig.
	Revue hebdomadaire de Chimie.	Paris	1869-1875	7	Mene.
82	Revue scientifique et industrielle.	Paris	1840-1844	16	De Quesneville.
	2nd Series.	Paris	1844-1847	15	De Quesneville.
	3rd Series.	Paris	1848-1851	9	De Quesneville.
	4th Series.	Paris	1852	1	De Quesneville.
	continued as:-				
	Moniteur Scientifique, 1st Series.	Paris	1857-1863	5	De Quesneville.
	2nd Series.	Paris	1864-1870	7	De Quesneville.
	3rd Series.	Paris	1871-1926	50+	—
	(Merged, 1927, in Rev. Chim. Ind.).				

No.	Title	Published from	Date	Vols.	Editor
83	Scheikundige onderzookingen, gedaan in het laboratorium der Utrechtsche Hoogeschool.	Rotterdam	1845-1876 Irreg.	17	Mulder et al.
84	Technisch-chemisches Jahrbuch.	Berlin	1830-1884+	5+	Bidermann.
85	Tekno-Kemisk Journal.	Stockholm	1847-1848	1	Alstrom.
86	Tidskrift for anvendt Chemi.	Kjøbenhavnl	1869-1870	1	Holm.
87	Tidskrift for Physik og Chemi samt diese videnskabers Anvendelse.	Kjøbenhavnl	1862-1870	12	Thomsen.
88	Tidskrift voor wetenschappelijke Pharmacie, 1st Series.	Voorburg	1849-1853	5	Haaxmann.
	2nd Series.	's Graven-hage	1854-1858	5	Haaxmann.
	3rd Series.	's Graven-hage	1859-1864	6	Haaxmann.
	4th Series	Gorinchem	1865-1873	9	Haaxmann.
89	Toegepaste Scheikunde	Vlaardingen	1865-1869	5	Opwyrda.
	2nd Series.	Vlaardingen	1870-1875	4	Opwyrda.
	continued as:-				
90	Maandblad voor toegepaste scheikunde.	Amsterdam	1876-1880+	5+	Opwyrda.
91	Ueber die neueren Gegenstande in der Chemie.	Breslau	1791-1802	11	Richter.
	Untersuchungen aus Liebig's Laboratorium.	Wien	1872	1	Liebig.
92	Viertel jahresschrift für technische Chemie.	Quedlinberg	1859-1869	19	Artus.
93	Zeitschrift für das chemische Grossgewerte.	Berlin	1876-1882	7	Post.
94	Zpravy spolku Chemiku ceskych.*	Prage	1872-1876	2	Safarik.

* It is thought that Casopis chemiku ceskych (1 Vol. 1870) is a logical predecessor of this, and there may have been sporadic numbers published after 1876.

AN ADDITIONAL EXAMPLE OF AN
ORGANIC CHEMICAL SEARCH

Subject:- The Nitration of Hexane.

It is assumed that the worker is about to commence some extensive work on the nitration of hexane, and that the literature search is a necessary preliminary. In this appendix is given an account of the steps leading to the establishment of a final list of references; a citation of all the abstracts in detail would be too lengthy a procedure for this short work, but the student is recommended to use the reference list as an exercise, and, by reading each of the abstracts and making notes of the salient points, to build up a full account of the subject.

It is first necessary to compile a word-list of headings under which a search of the indexes can be made. It is clear that the first point of search will be *Hexane, nitration of,* but, in addition, it will be advisable to search under *Nitration, of hexane,* since it does not follow that the same set of references will be found under both headings. This principle is well exemplified by the two search points, *Nitration, of paraffins,* and *Paraffins, nitration of.* Each of these headings is a proper point of search, but reference to Table I will shew that although the harvest of references under the two headings shews considerable overlap, there are several references under either entry, which do not appear in the complementary list; these are italicized in the Table. That this phenomenon is quite general, and not an accident in the searching of this particular subject can be realized from an inspection of Table II, where the corresponding data for the nitration of benzene is displayed.

Great care must be taken in comparing the entries at headings of slightly different implication; thus, in the case of the heading *Nitration, of hydrocarbons,* the simple converse

TABLE I

Volume	References under Paraffins, nitration of	References under Nitration, of paraffins
31	654,6190	654,6190
32	1648,P2143,835	1648,P2143,8357
33	532,P4601,6793, 5001,5003	532,P4601,6793 5001,5003
34	3235	-
35	-	7270,P465,P2158
36	-	-
37	6640	1376,6640
38	P756	-
39	906	906
40	5011	5011,2454
41	3810,5435,6526	3043
42	7261,7262,1003, 585,4913	585
43	4216,4629,5791	2220,4629,5791
44	1044,8360,1009, 1010	8360,1009
45	1311,9555	-
46	1308,7992,1024	1308,1024
47	2688	-
48	2758	-

TABLE II

Volume	References under Benzene, nitration of	References under Nitration, of benzene
31	2174,P5818,5573, 4285	2174
32	923,P3423,6638, 7830,6673	-
33	3781	-
34	2262,4673,7167	2262,7167
35	P938	P938
36	P96,2844,5465	2844,3418,5465
37	6550	-
40	269,P360	269

Volume	References under Benzene, nitration of	References under Nitration, of benzene
41	6897	-
42	P5050,P3778	-
43	7918	5731,4644
44	1045	-
45	2886,7538,10213	2886,10213
46	6876	6026,6876
47	2620,5821,6361	-
48	619,11480,12478	619,5214,12478

Hydrocarbons, nitration of, must, of course, be searched, but in addition the heading *Hydrocarbons, (aromatic) nitration of,* must also be searched. As the results of such a search are germane to the subject, they are shewn in Table III.

TABLE III

Vol.	References under Hydrocarbons, nitration of	References under Hydrocarbons, (aromatic) nitration of	References under Nitration, of hydrocarbons
31	-	5773,1820,P5818	1820,5818
32	-	P2541,P3423, 7829	P2541,P3423, 3964
33	-	P991,3781	P991
34	4673,P5464, P7295,7843	4742	3962,4742,5464, 7295,7843
35	4356	-	4356
36	779	-	779
37	6867	-	6867
38	951,P1749	-	951,P1749
39	906	-	906
41	-	-	6526,P6897,5435
42	7261,7262	59,3340,1605	7261,7262
43	P1561,3352, 5012,4216,6584	-	P1561,3352,4216 6584
44	1709,5829,P8942	1044	5829,P8942
45	P9816	-	P9816,6999
47	P2766,9252,3789	-	P2766,9252
48	P2758,P11480, P11790	-	P2758

In one index it will be found that under the heading *Nitration,* there are the following entries:-

Nitration,

· · ·

· · ·

· · ·

of hydrocarbons, review, 9252

· · ·

· · ·

· · ·

reviews, 11123,11601

hence, the importance of glancing through the whole entry to be sure that nothing is missed.

This peculiarity of indexes is a subject of which all users of indexes should be aware; the reasons which lie behind these discrepancies are complex, and it must not be thought that to point out their existence is intended as a criticism of the indexing of abstracts; the difficulties arise much earlier in the chain of causation, and are concerned, among other things, with the titles of original communications. The subject is too large to be discussed in detail here, but it may be illustrated, perhaps, by the following example: if a paper entitled *The Kinetics of Nitration* has in it references to the nitration of mesitylene, it is certain that the headings *Nitration, Mesitylene* and *Kinetics* will be entered in the index; on the other hand, the word *Hydrocarbon* has not, so far, appeared in this connexion; and it is improbable that it will be entered in the index. On the other hand, had the paper been entitled *Kinetics of Hydrocarbon Nitration* the index entry *Hydrocarbon* would have been assured.

It is an excellent idea to compile a word-list of all likely headings under which search should be made. Such a list is given below:-

Word-list for search on **Nitration of Hexane.**

Main Part.

Hexane, nitration of
Nitration, of hexane
Paraffins, nitration of
Nitration of paraffins

Hydrocarbons, nitration of
Nitration of hydrocarbons
Hexane,
 1-nitro
 2-nitro
 3-nitro
 —dinitro
 —trinitro
 chloronitro
 bromonitro
Hexene, nitration of
 nitro derivatives
*neo*Hexane, nitration of

Secondary Part.

Methylpentanes, nitration of
Pentanes, methyl nitration of
Butanes, dimethyl, nitration of

It will be noticed that this word-list is in two parts; the first part is concerned with entries having a direct application to the nitration of hexane; the second portion is a few suggested headings under which analogous reactions may be searched.

The next operation is to list all the references in **Chemical Abstracts** under these headings. At the same time, if this has not already been done, it is as well to extract the information available from **Beilstein,** and so obtain an historical background of the subject. The entries are to be found under the nitro-derivatives of hexane, and there is the following to be recorded:-

Beilstein. Vol. H I, p. 147.

1. *Worstall,* Am. Ch. J. *20*,207; *21*,219, obtained 1-nitro-hexane, by direct nitration of hexane.
2. *Konalov,* J. Russ. Phys.-Chem. Soc. *25*,476, isolated 2-nitrohexane by direct nitration of hexane.
3. *Henry,* Rec. Trav. Chim. *24*,360, obtained 1,1-dinitro-hexane by direct nitration.
4. *Auger,* Bl. [3],*23*,335, obtained a mononitrohexane from α-bromoœnanthic acid (K salt) and $NaNO_2$.
5. *Henry,* C. 1905;II,214; R. *24*,356, obtained 1-nitrohexane from α-iodohexane and $AgNO_2$ in ether.

6. *Chancel*, J. 1882,454, obtained dinitrohexane from methylhexylketone by nitration.
7. *Ponzio*, G. *31*,[II],406, obtained dinitrohexane by the nitration of methylhexylcarbinol.
8. *Ponzio*, J. Pr. [2],53,432, obtained dinitrohexane by nitration of œnanthol.

From these somewhat meagre data the following summary may be made:-

1-Nitrohexane, b_{765} 193-4°; b_{75} 112°; D^{20} 0·9488. Insol. water, easily sol. alcohol or ether. Colourless liquid.

2-Nitrohexane,   b. 176°; D^{20} 0·9357. Colourless liquid.

1,1-Dinitrohexane, a yellow oil.

There are no additional entries in the supplements to **Beilstein** under the nitrohexanes, so it must be presumed that after 1900 the substances were not investigated again until after 1929.

The full set of references from **Chemical Abstracts** is shewn in Table IV, and the next step will be to inspect each reference and if necessary, make notes on such as contain useful information; alternatively, a paper-print by diazotype or contact process can be made of the abstracts which are of use. In either case it is advisable to mount either the note or the copy on an individual card, and thus to make a card index of the subject. The cards can then be checked against **British Abstracts** and **Zentralblatt.** It is not proposed to reproduce such a series of entries here, but the student will find it interesting to complete the exercise.

The main original papers will now have to be read; after which the worker will be ready to plan his course of action; it will be clear that the procedure outlined will not have revealed everything that is known about the subject, but if conscientiously carried out nothing of first importance will have been overlooked.

TABLE IV

Subject	1927-1936	1937-1946	1947-1954
Hexane, nitration of	**28**:6707	**31**:3868,6190 **33**:532	-
Hexane, and NOCl	**30**:6703	-	-
Hexane, mononitro	-	**31**:690	**41**:1232,P4508 **42**:4912-3 **46**:2993 **48**:1812
Hexane, dinitro	**29**:3329	-	-
Hexane, 1-nitro, 6-phenyl	-	**31**:6190 **29**:3329	-
Hexane, chloronitro	**21**:2872-3	-	-
Hexane, methyl, dinitro	-	-	**44**:P1128,1010 **45**:5099
Nitration, of hexane } Nitration, of paraffins	-	**31**:P1820 **32**:P2451 P4323 **33**:9918, P3964 **34**:3062, P4724,P5464, P7295 **35**:435 **36**:P779 **37**:6867 **38**:951,P1749 **39**:906	**41**:6526,P6897, 5435 **42**:7261,7262, 6313 **43**:1561,3352, 4216,6584 **44**:1010 **45**:1311,9555 **46**:1308,7992,1024 **47**:2688,1726
Hydrocarbons, nitration of (additional refs.)	-	**34**:4673	(Pentane) **44**:1009
Nitration of haloethylenes	**26**:4029	-	-
Nitration of paraffins	**28**:P5830 **30**:2918	**31**:654,6190 **32**:1648,P2413,8537 **33**:532,P4601, P5001,P5003, 6793 **35**:P465, P2158,7270 **37**:1376,6640 **39**:906 **40**:5011,P2454	**41**:3043,P7409 **42**:585,801,3925, P5050,7583 **43**:P2220,4629 **44**:1009 **46**:1024,1038
Nitration with NO_2	-	**31**:3866	**42**:4906
Hexene, nitration of	-	-	-
Hexene-2, 2-nitro-	-	**38**:2007	**42**:2228 **44**:4412 **48**:8259
Hexene-3, 3-nitro-	-	**40**:P3126	**44**:2876
2-Hexanol, nitro	**24**:4001	-	-
Dimethylbutane, nitration of	-	**40**:4348	**44**:9922 **46**:4930 **48**:10536

APPENDIX III

JOURNAL YEARS AND VOLUME NUMBERS

The following enumeration and abbreviations are used throughout these tables, to conserve space:-

No.	Title	Abbrevn.
1	American Chemical Journal	A.C.J.
2	American Journal of Science	A.J.S.
3	Analyst	Anal.
4	Annalen (Liebig's)	Ann.
5	Annalen Supplements	Ann.S.
6	Annales de Chimie	Ann.C.
7	Annales de Physique	Ann.P.
8	Annales des Mines	Ann.M.
9	Archiv für experimentelle Pathologie und Pharmakologie	Ar.P.P.
10	Archiv de Pharmacie	A.P.
11	Atti del Reale Accademia dei Lincei	Atti.
12	Beilstein H.	Bei.H.
13	Beilstein E 1	Bei.E 1.
14	Beilstein E 2	Bei.E 2.
15	Beitrage zur chemischen Physiologie und Pathologie	Beit.
16	Berichte der deutschen chemischen Gesellschaft.	Ber.
17	Biochemical Journal	Bio.J.
18	Biochemische Zeitschrift	Bio.Z.
19	Bulletin de la Société chimique de France	Bull.
20	Chemical News	C.N.
21	Chemical Reviews	C.Rev.
22	Chemical Trade Journal	C.T.J.
23	Chemische Industrie	C.Ind.

No.	Title	Abbrevn.
24	Chemische Weekblad	C.W.
25	Chemiker Zeitung.	C.Ztg.
26	Comptes Rendus de l'Académie des Sciences.	C.R.
27	Dingler's Polytechnic Journal	Ding.
28	Friedlander's Fortschritte	Fort.
29	Gazzetta Chimica Italiana	Gazz.
30	Gilbert's Annalen.	Gilb.
31	Industrial and Engineering Chemistry	I.E.C.
32	Helvetica Chimica Acta	Helv.
33	Journal of the American Chemical Society	J.A.C.S.
34	Journal of Biological Chemistry	J.B.C.
35	Journal of The Chemical Society	J.
36	Journal of Organic Chemistry	J.O.C.
37	Journal de Pharmacie et de Chimie	J.Ph.
38	Journal of Physical Chemistry	J.P.C.
39	Journal für Praktische Chemie	J.Prak.
40	Journal of the Physical and Chemical Society of Russia	ψ
41	Journal of the Society of Chemical Industry	J.S.C.I.
42	Monatshefte für Chemie und Verwandte Theile anderer Wissenschaften	Monat.
43	Nature	Nat.
44	Organic Syntheses	O.S.
45	Pharmaceutische Zentralhalle	P.Z.
46	Philosophical Magazine	Phil.M.
47	Philosophical Transactions of the Royal Society of London	Phil.T.
48	Physical Review	P.R.
49	Physikalische Zeitschrift	P.Z.
50	Proceedings of the Chemical Society	P.Soc.
51	Proceedings of the Royal Society	P.Roy.S.
52	Recueil des Travaux Chimiques des Pays-Bas	Rec.
53	Sitzungsberichte der Akademie der Wissenschaften, Wien	Sitz.
54	Zeitschrift für analytische Chemie	Z.Anal.C.
55	Zeitschrift für angewandte Chemie	Z.Ang.C.
56	Zeitschrift für anorganische und allgemeine Chemie	Z.Anorg.
57	Zeitschrift für Elektrochemie	Z.El.C.

No.	Title	Abbrevn.
58	Zeitschrift für Krystallographie und Mineralogie	Z.Kryst.
59	Zeitschrift für physikalische Chemie . .	Z.φ.X.
60	Zeitschrift für physiologische Chemie . .	Z.Ph.C.
61	British (chemical) Abstracts	B.A.
62	Chemical Abstracts	C.A.
63	Chemisches C(Z)entralblatt	Z.

In the tables below the small superior figures are in reference to the notes at the end.

TABLES

No.	Name	1800	1801	1802	1803	1804
6	Ann.C.	[1][2]32-35	36-39	40-43	44-47	48-51
30	Gilb.	4-6[10]	7-9	10-12	13-15	16-18
46	Phil.M.	[1][13] 5-8	8-11	11-14	14-17	17-20
47	Phil.T.[14]	90	91	92	93	94

		1805	1806	1807	1808	1809
6	Ann.C.	[1] 52-55	56-60	61-64	65-68	69-72
30	Gilb.	19-21	22-24	25-27	28-30	31-33
37	J.Ph.					[1] 1
46	Phil.M.	[1] 20-23	23-26	26-29	29-32	33,34
47	Phil.T.	95	96	97	98	99

		1810	1811	1812	1813	1814
6	Ann.C.	[1] 73-76	77-80	81-84	85-88	89-92
30	Gilb.	34-36	37-39	40-42	43-45	46-48
37	J.Ph.	[1] 2	3	4	5	6
46	Phil.M.	[1] 35,36	37,38	39,40	41,42	43,44
47	Phil.T.	100	101	102	103	104

		1815	1816	1817	1818	1819
2	A.J.S.	[1]				1
6	Ann.C.	[1] 93-96 }	[2]1-3	4-6	7-9	10-12
7	Ann.P.					
8	Ann.M.	[1]		1,2	3	4
30	Gilb.	49-51	52-54	55-57	58-60	61-63
37	J.Ph.	[2] 1	2	3	4	5
46	Phil.M.	[1] 45,46	47,48	49,50	51,52	53,54
47	Phil.T.	105	106	107	108	109

No.	Name		1820	1821	1822	1823	1824
2	A.J.S.	[1]	2	3	4,5	6	7,8
6&7	Ann.C.P.	[2]	13-15	16-18	19-21	22-24	25-27
8	Ann.M.	[1]	5	6	7	8	9
10	A.P.	[1]			1,2	3-6	7-10
27	D.P.J.		1-3	4-6	7-9	10-12	13-15
30	Gilb.		64-66	67-69	70-72	73-75	76/1-2*
37	J.Ph.	[2]	6	7	8	9	10
46	Phil.M.	[1]	55,56	57,58	59,60	61,62	63,64
47	Phil.T.		110	111	112	113	114

No.	Name		1825	1826	1827	1828	1829
2	A.J.S.	[1]	9	10,11	12	13,14	15,16
6&7	Ann.C.P.	[2]	28-30	31-33	34-36	37-39	40-42
8	Ann.M.	[1]	10,11	12,13	[2]1,2	3,4	5,6
10	A.P.	[1]	11-14	15-19	20-23	24-26	27-30
27	D.P.J.		16-18	19-22	23-26	27-30	31-34
30	Pogg.		3-5	6-8	9-11	12-14	15-17
37	J.Ph.	[2]	11	12	13	14	15
46	Phil.M.	[1]	65,66	67,68	[2]1,2	3,4	5,6
47	Phil.T.		115	116	117	118	119

No.	Name		1830	1831	1832	1833	1834
2	A.J.S.	[1]	17,18	19,20	21,22	23,24	25,26
4	Ann.				1-4	5-8	9-12
6&7	Ann.C.P.	[2]	43-45	46-48	49-51	52-55	56,57
8	Ann.M.	[2]	7,8	.	[3]1,2	3,4	5,6
10	A.P.	[1]	31-34	35-39	40-43	44-47	48-50
27	D.P.J.		35-38	39-42	43-47	48-50	51-54
30	Pogg.		18-20	21-23	24-26	27-29	30-33
37	J.Ph.	[2]	16	17	18	19	20
39	J.Prak.	[1]					1-3
46	Phil.M.	[2]	7,8	9,10	11[3]1	2,3	4,5
47	Phil.T.		120	121	122	123	124
51	P.Roy.S.				1	2	-

No.	Name		1835	1836	1837	1838	1839
2	A.J.S.	[1]	28,29	30,31	32,33	34,35	36,37
4	Ann.		13-16	17-20	21-24	25-28	29-32
6&7	Ann.C.P.	[2]	58-60	61-63	64-66	67-69	70-72
8	Ann.M.	[3]	7,8	9,10	11,12	13,14	15,16
10	A.P.	[1]	1-4	5-8	9-12	13-16	17-20

* Continued as Poggendorf's Annalen.

No.	Name		1835	1836	1837	1838	1839
26	C.R.		1	2,3	4,5	6,7	8,9
27	D.P.J.		55-58	59-62	63-66	67-70	71-74
30	Pogg.		34-36	37-39	40-42	43-45	46-48
37	J.Ph.	[2]	21	22	23	24	25
39	J.Prak.	[1]	4-6	7-9	10-12	13-15	16-18
46	Phil.M.	[3]	6,7	8,9	10,11	12,13	14,15
47	Phil.T.		125	126	127	128	129
51	P.Roy.S.		-	-	3	-	-

No.	Name		1840	1841	1842	1843	1844
2	A.J.S.	[1]	38,39	40,41	42,43	44,45	46,47
4	Ann.		33-36	37-40	41-44	45-48	49-52
6&7	Ann.C.P.	[2]	73-75	[3]1-3	4-6	7-9	10-12
8	Ann.M.	[3]	17,18	19,20	[4]1,2	3,4	5,6
10	A.P.	[2]	21-24	25-28	29-32	33-36	37-40
20	C.N.		The Chemical Gazette			(1)	(2)
26	C.R.		10,11	12,13	14,15	16,17	18,19
27	D.P.J.		75-78	79-82	83-86	87-90	91-94
30	Pogg.		49-51	52-54	55-57	58-60	61-63
35	J.			—— i ——			
37	J.Ph.	[2]	26	27	[3]1,2	3,4	5,6
39	J.Prak.	[1]	19-21	22-24	25-27	28-30	31-33
46	Phil.M.	[3]	16,17	18,19	20,21	22,23	24,25
47	Phil.T.		130	131	132	133	134
51	P.Roy.S.		-	-	-	4	-

No.	Name		1845	1846	1847	1848	1849
2	A.J.S.	[1]	48-50	[2]1,2	3,4	5,6	7,8
4	Ann.		53-56	57-60	61-64	65-68	69-72
6&7	Ann.C.P.	[3]	13-15	16-18	19-21	22-24	25-27
8	Ann.M.	[4]	7,8	9,10	11,12	13,14	15,16
10	A.P.	[2]	41-44	45-48	49-52	53-56	57-60
20	C.N.		(3)	(4)	(5)	(6)	(7)
26	C.R.		20,21	22,23	24,25	26,27	28,29
27	D.P.J.		95-98	99-102	103-106	107-110	111-114
30	Pogg.		64-66	67-69	70-72	73-75	76-78
35	J.		ii —— | iii –][21]	1	1,2	2,3
37	J.Ph.	[3]	7,8	9,10	11,12	13,14	15,16
39	J.Prak.	[1]	34-36	37-39	40-42	43-45	46-48
46	Phil.M.	[3]	26,27	28,29	30,31	32,33	34,35
47	Phil.T.		135	136	137	138	139
51	P.Roy.S.		-	-	-	-	-
53	Sitz.					1	2,3

No.	Name		1850	1851	1852	1853	1854
2	A.J.S.	[2]	9,10	11,12	13,14	15,16	17,18
4	Ann.		73-76	77-80	81-84	85-88	89-92
6&7	Ann.C.P.	[3]	28-30	31-33	34-36	37-39	40-42
8	Ann.M.	[4]	17,18	19,20	[5]1,2	3,4	5,6
10	A.P.	[2]	61-64	65-68	69-72	73-76	77-80
11	Atti.	[1]	-	1	4,5	-	-
20	C.N.		(8)	(9)	(10)	(11)	(12)
26	C.R.		30,31	32,33	34,35	36,37	38,39
27	D.P.J.		115-118	119-122	123-126	127-130	131-134
30	Pogg.		79-81	82-84	85-87	88-90	91-93
35	J.		3	4	5	6	7
37	J.Ph.	[3]	17,18	19,20	21,22	23,24	25,26
39	J.Prak.	[1]	49-51	52-54	55-57	58-60	61-63
46	Phil.M.	[3]	36,37	[4]1,2	3,4	5,6	7,8
47	Phil.T.		140	141	142	143	144
51	P.Roy.S.		-	5	-	-	6,7
53	Sitz.		4,5	6,7	8,9	10,11	12-14

No.	Name		1855	1856	1857	1858	1859
2	A.J.S.	[2]	19,20	21,22	23,24	25,26	27,28
4	Ann.		93-96	97-100	101-104	105-108	109-112
6&7	Ann.C.P.	[3]	43-45	46-48	49-51	52-54	55-57
8	Ann.M.	[5]	7,8	9,10	11,12	13,14	15,16
10	A.P.	[2]	81-84	85-88	89-92	93-96	97-100
11	Atti.		6	7,10	11	-	12
19	Bull.	[1]					1
20	C.N.		(13)	(14)	(15)	(16)	(17)
26	C.R.		40,41	42,43	44,45	46,47	48,49
27	D.P.J.		135-138	139-142	143-146	147-150	151-154
30	Pogg.		94-96	97-99	100-102	103-105	106-108
35	J.		8	9	10	11	12
37	J.Ph.	[3]	27,28	29,30	31,32	33,34	35,36
39	J.Prak.	[1]	64-66	67-69	70-72	73-75	76-78
46	Phil.M.	[4]	9,10	11,12	13,14	15,16	17,18
47	Phil.T.		145	146	147	148	149
51	P.Roy.S.		7	8	9 ———	9 ———	9,10
53	Sitz.		15-18	19-22	23-27	28-33	34-38

No.	Name	1860	1861	1862	1863	1864
2	A.J.S.	[2] 29,30	31,32	33,34	35,36	37,38
4	Ann.	113-116	117-120	121-124	125-128	129-132
5	Ann.S.	1	2 —— 2		3 —— 3,4	
6&7	Ann.C.P.	[3] 58-60	61-63	64-66	67-69	[4]1-3
8	Ann.M.	[5] 17,18	19,20	[6]1,2	3,4	5,6
10	A.P.	[2]101-104	105-108	109-112	113-116	117-120
11	Atti.	[1] 13	14	15	16	17
19	Bull.	[1] 2	3	4	5	[2]1,2
20	C.N.	(17) 1,2	3,4	5,6	7,8	9,10
26	C.R.	50,51	52,53	54,55	56,57	58,59
27	D.P.J.	155-158	159-162	163-166	167-170	171-174
30	Pogg.	109-111	112-114	115-117	118-120	121-123
35	J.	13	14	15	16	17
37	J.Ph.	[3] 37,38	39,40	41,42	43,44	45,46
39	J.Prak.	[1] 79-81	82-84	85-87	88-90	91-93
46	Phil.M.	[4] 19,20	21,22	23,24	25,26	27,28
47	Phil.T.	150	151	152	153	154
51	P.Roy.S.	10,11	11	11,12	12,13	13
53	Sitz.	39-42	43	44,45	46-48	49
54	Z.Anal.C.			1[18]	2	3

No.	Name	1865	1866	1867	1868	1869
2	A.J.S.	[2] 39,40	41,42	43,44	45,46	47,48
4	Ann.	133-136	137-140	141-144	145-148	149-152
5	Ann.S.	4	5	6	-	7
6&7	Ann.C.P.	[4] 4-6	7-9	10-12	13-15	16-18
8	Ann.M.	[6] 7,8	9-10	11,12	13,14	15,16
10	A.P.	121-124	125-128	129-132	133-136	137-140
11	Atti.	[1] 18	19	20	21	22,23
16	Ber.				1	2
19	Bull.	[2] 3,4	5,6	7,8	9,10	11,12
20	C.N.	11,12	13,14	15,16	17,18	19,20
26	C.R.	60,61	62,63	64,65	66,67	68,69
27	D.P.J.	175-178	179-182	183-186	187-190	191-194
30	Pogg.	124-126	127-129	130-132	133-135	136-138
35	J.	18	19	20	21	22
37	J.Ph.	[4] 1,2	3,4	5,6	7,8	9,10
39	J.Prak.	[1] 94-96	97-99	100-102	103-105	106-108
40	ψ					1
43	Nat.					1

No.	Name	1865	1866	1867	1868	1869
46	Phil.M.	[4] 29,30	31,32	33,34	35,36	37,38
47	Phil.T.	155	156	157	158	159
51	P.Roy.S.	14	15	15,16	16,17	17,18
53	Sitz.	50-52	53,54	55,56	57,58	59,60
54	Z.Anal.C.	4	5	6	7	8

No.	Name	1870	1871	1872	1873	1874
2	A.J.S.	[2] 49,50	[3]1,2	3,4	5,6	7,8
4	Ann.	153-156	157-160	161-164	165-170	171-174
5	Ann.S.	-	8	Ceased.		
6&7	Ann.C.P.	[4] 19,20	22-24	25-27	28-30	[5]1-3
8	Ann.M.	[6] 17,18	19,20	[7]1,2	3,4	5,6
9	Ar.P.P.				1	2
10	A.P.	141-144	145-148	149-151[1]	201-203	204,205
11	Atti.	[1] -	24	25	3,26	8,9
16	Ber.	3	4	5	6	7
19	Bull.	[2] 13,14	15,16	17,18	19,20	21,22
20	C.N.	21,22	23,24	25,26	27,28	29,30
26	C.R.	70,71	72,73	74,75	76,77	78,79
27	D.P.J.	195-198	199-202	203-206	207-210	211-214
29	Gazz.		1	2	3	4
30	Pogg.	139-141	142-144	145-147	148-150	151-153
35	J.	23	24	25	26	27
37	J.Ph.	[4] 11,12	13,14	15,16	17,18	19,20
39	J.Prak.	[2] 1,2	3,4	5,6	7,8	9,10
40	ψ	2	3	4	5	6
43	Nat.	1-3	3-5	5-7	7-9	9-11
46	Phil.M.	[4] 39,40	41,42	43,44	45,46	47,48
47	Phil.T.	160	161	162	163	164
51	P.Roy.S.	18,19	19,20	20,21	21,22	22,23
53	Sitz.	61,62	63,64	65,66	67,68	69,70
54	Z.Anal.C.	9	10	11	12	13

No.	Name	1875	1876	1877	1878	1879
2	A.J.S.	[3] 9,10	11,12	13,14	15,16	17,18
3	Anal.		1	2	3	4
4	Ann.	175-179	180-183	184-189	190-194	195-199
6&7	Ann.C.P.	[5] 4-6	7-9	10-12	13-15	16-18
8	Ann.M.	[7] 7,8	9,10	11,12	13,14	15,16
9	Ar.P.P.	3,4	5	6,7	8,9	10,11

No.	Name	1875	1876	1877	1878	1879
10	A.P.	206,207	208,209	210,211	212,213	214,215
11	Atti.	[2] 1,2	3	[3] 1	2	3,4
16	Ber.	8	9	10	11	12
19	Bull.	[2] 23,24	25,26	27,28	29,30	31,32
20	C.N.	31,32	33,34	35,36	37,38	39,40
25	C.Ztg.			1	2	3
26	C.R.	80,81	82,83	84,85	86,87	88,89
27	D.P.J.	215-218	219-222	223-226	227-230	231-234
29	Gazz.	5	6	7	8	9
30	Pogg.	154-156	157-159	160*1,2	3-5	6-8
33	J.A.C.S.					1
35	L.	28	29,30	31,32	33,34	35,36
37	J.Ph.	[4] 21,22	23,24	25,26	27,28	29,30
39	J.Prak.	[2] 11,12	13,14	15,16	17,18	19,20
40	ψ	7	8	9	10	11
43	Nat.	11-13	13-15	15-17	17-19	19-21
46	Phil.M.	[4] 49,50	[5]1,2	3,4	5,6	7,8
47	Phil.T.	165	166	167	168,169	170
51	P.Roy.S.	23,24	24,25	25,26	27,28	28-30
53	Sitz.	71,72	73,74	75,76	77,78	79,80
54	Z.Anal.C.	14	15	16	17	18
58	Z.Kryst.			1	2	3
60	Z.Ph.C.			1	1,2	2,3

No.	Name	1880	1881	1882	1883	1884
1	A.C.J.	1,2	2,3	3,4	4,5	5,6
2	A.J.S.	[3] 19,20	21,22	23,24	25,26	27,28
3	Anal.	5	6	7	8	9
4	Ann.	200-205	206-210	211-215	216-221	222-226
6&7	Ann.C.P.	[5] 19-21	22-24	25-27	28-30	[6]1-3
8	Ann.M.	[7] 17,18	19,20	[8]1,2	3,4	5,6
9	Ar.P.P.	12	13,14	15	16,17	18
10	A.P.	216,217	218,219	220	221	222
11	Atti.	[2] 5-7	-	-	8	-
		[3] 5-8	9-11	12-13	14-16,18	17,19
12	Bei.H	———— 1st Edn. ————				
16	Ber.	13	14	15	16	17
19	Bull.	[2] 33,34	35,36	37,38	39,40	41,42
20	C.N.	41,42	43,44	45,46	47,48	49,50
25	C.Ztg.	4	5	6	7	8

* Continued as Wiedemann's Annalen

No.	Name	1880	1881	1882	1883	1884
26	C.R.	90,91	92,93	94,95	96,97	98,99
27	D.P.J.	235-238	239-242	243-246	247-250	251-254
29	Gazz.	10	11	12	13	14
30	Wied.	9-11	12-14	15-17	18-20	21-23
33	J.A.C.S.	2	3	4	5	6
35	J.	37,38	39,40	41,42	43,44	45,46
37	J.Ph.	[5] 1,2	3,4	5,6	7,8	9,10
39	J.Prak.	[2] 21,22	23,24	25,26	27,28	29,30
40	ψ	12	13	14	15	16
41	J.S.C.I.			1	2	3
42	Monat.	1	2	3	4	5
43	Nat.	21-23	23-25	25-27	27-29	29-31
46	Phil.M.	[5] 9,10	11,12	13,14	15,16	17,18
47	Phil.T.	171	172	173	174	175
51	P.Roy.S.	30,31	31-33	33,34	34-36	36-38
52	Rec.			1	2	3
53	Sitz.	81,82	83,84	85,86	87,88	89,90
54	Z.Anal.C.	19	20	21	22	23
58	Z.Kryst.	4	5	6	7	8,9
60	Z.Ph.C.	4,5	5,6	6,7	7,8	8,9

No.	Name	1885	1886	1887	1888	1889
1	A.C.J.	6,7	7,8	9	10	11
2	A.J.S.	[3] 29,30	31,32	33,34	35,36	37,38
3	Anal.	10	11	12	13	14
4	Ann.	227-231	232-236	237-242	243-249	250-255
6&7	Ann.C.P.	[6] 4-6	7-9	10-12	13-15	16-18
8	Ann.M.	[8] 7,8	9,10	11,12	13,14	15,16
9	Ar.P.P.	19	20,21	22,23	24	25
10	A.P.	223	224	225	226	227
11	Atti.	[4] 1	2	$\{^{[2]4}_{[4]3}\}$	[4] 4	5
12	Bei.H.		——————— 2nd Edn. ———————			
16	Ber.	18	19	20	21	22
19	Bull.	[2] 43,44	45,46	47,48	49,50	[3]1,2
20	C.N.	51,52	53,54	55,56	57,58	59,60
22	C.T.J.			1	2,3	4,5
25	C.Ztg.	9	10	11	12	13
26	C.R.	100,101	102,103	104,105	106,107	108,109
27	D.P.J.	255-258	259-262	263-266	267-270	271-274

No.	Name		1885	1886	1887	1888	1889
29	Gazz.		15	16	17	18	19
30	Wied.		24-26	27-29	30-32	33-35	36-38
33	J.A.C.S.		7	8	9	10	11
35	J.		47,48	49,50	51,52	53,54	55,56
37	J.Ph.	[5]	11,12	13,14	15,16	17,18	19,20
39	J.Prak.	[2]	31,32	33,34	35,36	37,38	39,40
40	ψ		17	18	19	20	21
41	J.S.C.I.		4	5	6	7	8
42	Monat.		6	7	8	9	10
43	Nat.		31-33	33-35	35-37	37-39	39-41
46	Phil.M.	[5]	19,20	21,22	23,24	25,26	27,28
47	Phil.T.		176	177	178	179	180
50	P.Soc.		1	2	3	4	5
51	P.Roy.S.		38,39	40,41	42,43	43-45	45-47
52	Rec.		4	5	6	7	8
53	Sitz.		91,92	93,94	95,96	97	98
54	Z.Anal.C.		24	25	26	27	28
55	Z.Ang.C.					1	2
58	Z.Kryst.		10	11	12	13,14	15
59	Z.ϕ.X.				1	2	3,4
60	Z.Ph.C.		9,10	10,11	11,12	12,13	13,14

No.	Name		1890	1891	1892	1893	1894
1	A.C.J.		12	13	14	15	16
2	A.J.S.	[3]	39,40	41,42	43,44	45,46	47,48
3	Anal.		15	16	17	18	19
4	Ann.		256-260	261-266	267-271	272-277	278-283
6&7	Ann.C.P.	[6]	19-21	22-24	25-27	28-30	[7]1-3
8	Ann.M.	[8]	17,18	19,20	[9]1,2	3,4	5,6
9	Ar.P.P.		26,27	28	29,30	31,32	33,34
10	A.P.		228	229	230	231	232
11	Atti.	[4]	6	7	[5]1	2	3
12	Bei.H.		—— 2nd Edn. ——		—————— 3rd Edn. ——————		
16	Ber.		23	24	25	26	27
19	Bull.	[3]	3,4	5,6	7,8	9,10	11,12
20	C.N.		61,62	63,64	65,66	67,68	69,70
22	C.T.J.		6,7	8,9	10,11	12,13	14,15
25	C.Ztg.		14	15	16	17	18
26	C.R.		110,111	112,113	114,115	116,117	118,119
27	D.P.J.		275-278	279-282	283-286	287-290	291-294

No.	Name	1890	1891	1892	1893	1894
28	Fort.		——— III	———		—IV—
29	Gazz.	20	21	22	23	24
30	Wied.	[3] 39-41	42-44	45-47	48-50	51-53
33	J.A.C.S.	12	13	14	15	16
35	J.	57,58	59,60	61,62	63,64	65,66
37	J.Ph.	[5] 21,22	23,24	25,26	27,28	29,30
39	J.Prak.	[2] 41,42	43,44	45,46	47,48	49,50
40	ψ	22	23	24	25	26
41	J.S.C.I.	9	10	11	12	13
42	Monat.	11	12	13	14	15
43	Nat.	41-43	43-45	45-47	47-49	49-51
46	Phil.M.	[5] 29,30	31,32	33,34	35,36	37,38
47	Phil.T.	181	182	183	184	185
50	P.Soc.	6	7	8	9	10
51	P.Roy.S.	47-49	49,50	50-52	52-54	55-57
52	Rec.	9	10	11	12	13
53	Sitz.	99	100	101	102	103
54	Z.Anal.C.	29	30	31	32	33
55	Z.Ang.C.	3	4	5	6	7
56	Z.Anorg.			1,2	3,4	5-7
57	Z.El.C.					1
58	Z.Kryst.	16,17	18,19	20	21	22,23
59	Z.ϕ.X.	5,6	7,8	9,10	11,12	13-15
60	Z.Ph.C.	14,15	15,16	16,17	17,18	18,19

		1895	1896	1897	1898	1899
1	A.C.J.	17	18	19	20	21,22
2	A.J.S.	[3] 49,50	[4]1,2	3,4	5,6	7,8
3	Anal.	20	21	22	23	24
4	Ann.	284-288	289-293	294-298	299-303	304-309
6&7	Ann.C.P.	[7] 4-6	7-9	10-12	13-15	16-18
8	Ann.M.	[9] 7,8	9,10	11,12	13,14	15,16
9	Ar.P.P.	35,36	37	38,39	40,41	42
10	A.P.	233	234	235	236	237
11	Atti.	[5] 4	5	6	7	8
12	Bei.H.		——— 3rd Edn.	———		
16	Ber.	28	29	30	31	32
19	Bull.	[3] 13,14	15,16	17,18	19,20	21,22
20	C.N.	71,72	73,74	75,76	77,78	79,80
22	C.T.J.	16,17	18,19	20,21	22,23	24,25

No.	Name	1895	1896	1897	1898	1899
25	C.Ztg.	19	20	21	22	23
26	C.R.	120,121	122,123	124,125	126,127	128,129
27	D.P.J.	295-298	299-302	303-306	307-310	311-314
28	Fort.	——— IV ———			——— V ———	
29	Gazz.	25	26	27	28	29
30	Wied.	[3] 54-56	57-59	60-63	64-66	67-69*
33	J.A.C.S.	17	18	19	20	21
35	J.	67,68	69,70	71,72	73,74	75,76
37	J.Ph.	[6] 1,2	3,4	5,6	7,8	9,10
38	J.P.C.			1	2	3
39	J.Prak.	[2] 51,52	53,54	55,56	57,58	59,60
40	ψ	27	28	29	30	31
41	J.S.C.I.	14	15	16	17	18
42	Monat.	16	17	18	19	20
43	Nat.	51-53	53-55	55-57	57-59	59-61
46	Phil.M.	[5] 39,40	41,42	43,44	45,46	47,48
47	Phil.T.	186	187,188	189,190	191	192,193
48	P.R.	[1] 1	2,3	4,5	6,7	8,9
50	P.Soc.	11	12	13	14	15
51	P.Roy.S.	57-59	59,60	60-62	62-64	64-66
52	Rec.	14	15	16	17	18
53	Sitz.	104	105	106	107	108
54	Z.Anal.C.	34	35	36	37	38
55	Z.Ang.C.	8	9	10	11	12
56	Z.Anorg.	8-10	11,12	13-15	16-18	19-21
57	Z.El.C.	1,2	2,3	3,4	4,5	5,6
58	Z.Kryst.	24	25,26	27,28	29	30,31
59	Z.φ.X.	16-18	19-21	22-24	25-27	28-31
60	Z.Ph.C.	20,21	21,22	22,23	24-26	26-28

		1900	1901	1902	1903	1904
1	A.C.J.	23,24	25,26	27,28	29,30	31,32
2	A.J.S.	[4] 9,10	11,12	13,14	15,16	17,18
3	Anal.	25	26	27	28	29
4	Ann.	310-313	314-319	320-325	326-329	330-337
6&7	Ann.C.P.	[7] 19-21	22-24	25-27	28-30	[8]1-3
8	Ann.M.	[9] 17,18	19,20	[10] 1,2	3,4	5,6
9	Ar.P.P.	43,44	45,46	47,48	49,50	51,52
10	A.P.	238	239	240	241	242

No.	Name		1900	1901	1902	1903	1904
11	Atti.	[5]	9	10	11	12	13
15	Beit.					1,2	3
16	Ber.		33	34	35	36	37
19	Bull.	[3]	23,24	25,26	27,28	29,30	31,32
20	C.N.		81,82	83,84	85,86	87,88	89,90
22	C.T.J.		26,27	28,29	30,31	32,33	34,35
25	C.Ztg.		24	25	26	27	28
26	C.R.		130,131	132,133	134,135	136,137	138,139
27	D.P.J.		315	316	317	318	319
29	Gazz.		30	31	32	33	34
30	A.Phys.	[4]	1-3	4-6	7-9	10-12	13-15
33	J.A.C.S.		22	23	24	25	26
35	J.		77,78	79,80	81,82	83,84	85,86
37	J.Ph.	[6]	11,12	13,14	15,16	17,18	19,20
38	J.P.C.		4	5	6	7	8
39	J.Prak.	[2]	61,62	63,64	65,66	67,68	69,70
40	ψ		32	33	34	35	36
41	J.S.C.I.		19	20	21	22	23
42	Monat.		21	22	23	24	25
43	Nat.		61-63	63-65	65-67	67-69	69-71
46	Phil.M.	[5]	49,50	[6]1,2	3,4	5,6	7,8
47	Phil.T.		194,195	196,197	198,199	200-202	203
48	P.R.	[1]	10,11	12,13	14,15	16,17	18,19
50	P.Soc.		16	17	18	19	20
51	P.Roy.S.		66,67	68,69	69,70	71,72	72-74
52	Rec.		19	20	21	22	23
53	Sitz.		109	110	111	112	113
54	Z.Anal.C.		39	40	41	42	43
55	Z.Ang.C.		13	14	15	16	17
56	Z.Anorg.		22	23-28	29-32	33-36	37-42
57	Z.El.C.		6,7	7	8	9	10
58	Z.Kryst.		32,33	34	35,36	37	38,39
59	Z.ϕ.X.		32-35	36-38	39-41	42-46	47-49
60	Z.Ph.C.		28-30	31-33	34-36	37-39	40-42

No.	Name	1905	1906	1907	1908	1909	1910	1911	1912	1913
1	A.C.J.	33,34	35,36	37,38	39,40	41,42	43,44	45,46	47,48	49,50*
2	A.J.S.	[4] 19,20	21,22	23,24	25,26	27,28	29,30	31,32	33,34	35,36
3	Anal.	30	31	32	33	34	35	36	37	38
4	Ann.	338-343	344-350	351-357	358-363	364-371	372-377	378-385	386-394	395-401
6&7	Ann.C.P.	[8] 4-6	7-9	10-12	13-15	16-18	19-21	22-24	25-27	28-30
8	Ann.M.	[10] 7,8	9,10	11,12	13,14	15,16	17,18.	19,20	[11] 1,2	3,4
9	Ar.P.P.	52,53	54,55	56,57	58,59	60,61	62,63	64-66	66-70	71-74
10	A.P.	243	244	245	246	247	248	249	250	251
11	Atti.	[5] 14	15	16	17	18	19	20	21	22
15	Beit.	4,5	6	7,8	9,10	11	Ceased.			
16	Ber.	38	39	40	41	42	43	44	45	46
17	Bio.J.		1	2	3	4	-	5	6	7
18	Bio.Z.		1	2-6	7-14	15-23	24-29	30-37	38-47	48-57
19	Bull.	[3] 33,34	35,36	[4]1,2	2,4	5,6	7,8	9,10	11,12	13,14
20	C.N.	91,92	93,94	95,96	97,98	99,100	101,102	103,104	105,106	107,108
22	C.T.J.	36,37	38,39	40,41	42,43	44,45	46,47	48,49	50,51	52,53
25	C.Ztg.	29	30	31	32	33	34	35	36	37
26	C.R.	140,141	142,143	144,145	146,147	148,149	150,151	152,153	154,155	156,157
27	D.P.J.	320	321	322	323	324	325	326	327	328
29	Gazz.	35	36	37	38	39	40	41	42	43
30	A.Phys.	[4] 16-18	19-21	22-24	25-27	28-30	31-33	34-36	37-39	40-42
31	I.E.C.					1	2	3	4	5

* Ceased and merged in the J.A.C.S.

		1905	1906	1907	1908	1909	1910	1911	1912	1913
33	J.A.C.S.	27	28	29	30	31	32	33	34	35
34	J.B.C.		1	2,3	4	5,6	7	8,9	10-12	13-16
35	J.	[6] 87,88	89,90	91,92	93,94	95,96	97,98	99,100	101,102	103,104
37	J.Ph.	21,22	23,24	25,26	27,28	29,30	[7]1,2	3,4	5,6	7,8
38	J.P.C.	9	10	11	12	13	14	15	16	17
39	J.Prak.	[2] 71,72	73,74	75,76	77,78	79,80	81,82	83,84	85,86	87,88
40	ψ	37	38	39	40	41	42	43	44	45
41	J.S.C.I.	24	25	26	27	28	29	30	31	32
42	Monat.	26	27	28	29	30	31	32	33	34
43	Nat.	71-73	73-75	75-77	77-79	79-82	82-85	85-88	88-90	90-92
46	Phil.M.	[6] 9-10	11,12	13,14	15,16	17,18	19,20	21,22	23,24	25,26
47	Phil.T.	204,205	206	207	207-209	209,210	210	210,211	211,212	212,213
48	P.R.	[1] 20,21	22,23	24,25	26,27	28,29	30,31	32,33	34,35	[2]1,2
50	P.Soc.	21	22	23	24	25	26	27	28	29
51	P.Roy.S.	74-76	77,78	78-80	80,81	82,83	83,84	84-86	86,87	88,89
52	Rec.	24	25	26	27	28	29	30	31	32
53	Sitz.	114	115	116	117	118	119	120	121	122
54	Z.Anal.C.	44	45	46	47	48	49	50	51	52
55	Z.Ang.C.	18	19	20	21	22	23	24	25	26
56	Z.Anorg.	43-47	48-51	52-55	56-60	61-64	65-68	69-72	73-78	79-83
57	Z.El.C.	11	12	13	14	15	16	17	18	19
58	Z.Kryst.	40	41	42,43	44,45	46	47	48,49	50	51,52
59	Z.φ.X.	50-53	54-56	57-60	61-64	65-69	70-74	75-77	78-80	81-85
60	Z.Ph.C.	93-95	96,97	98-100	101-103	104-107	108-111	112-117	118-123	124-131

No.	Name	1914	1915	1916	1917	1918	1919	1920	1921	1922
2	A.J.S.	[4] 37,38	39,40	41,42	43,44	45,46	47,48	49,50	[5]1,2	3,4
3	Anal.	39	40	41	42	43	44	45	46	47
4	Ann.	402-406	407-410	411	412,413	414-417	418,419	420,421	422-425	426-429
6&7	Ann.C.P.	[9] 1,2	3,4	5,6	7,8	9,10	11,12	13,14	15,16	17,18
8	Ann.M.	[11] 5,6	7,8	9,10	11,12	13,14	15,16	17,18	19,20	[12] 1,2
9	Ar.P.P.	75-77	78	79	80,81	82,83	84	85-88	89-91	92-95
10	A.P.	252	253	254	255	256	257	258	259	260
11	Atti.	[5] 23	24	25	26	27	28	29	30	31
12	Bei.H.				4th Edn.——1		-	2	3	4
16	Ber.	47	48	49	50	51	52	53	54	55
17	Bio.J.	8	9	10	11	12	13	14	15	16
18	Bio.Z.	58-67	68-71	72-77	78-84	85-92	93-100	101-112	113-126	127-133
19	Bull.	[4] 15,16	17,18	19,20	21,22	23,24	25,26	27,28	29,30	31,32
20	C.N.	109,110	111,112	113,114	115,116	117	118,119	120,121	122,123	124,125
22	C.T.J.	54,55	56,57	58,59	60,61	62,63	64,65	66,67	68,69	70,71
24	C.W.	11	12	13	14	15	16	17	18	19
25	C.Ztg.	38	39	40	41	42	43	44	45	46
26	C.R.	160,161	162,163	164,165	166,167	168,169	170,171	172,173	174,175	176,177
27	D.P.J.	329	330	331	332	333	334	335	336	337
29	Gazz.	44	45	46	47	48	49	50	51	52
30	A.Phys.	43-45	46-48	49-51	52-54	55-57	58-60	61-63	64-66	67-69
31	I.E.C.	6	7	8	9	10	11	12	13	14
32	Helv.					1	2	3	4	5
33	J.A.C.S.	36	37	38	39	40	41	42	43	44

		1914	1915	1916	1917	1918	1919	1920	1921	1922
34	J.B.C.	17-19	20-23	24-28	29-32	33-36	37-40	41-44	45-49	50-54
35	J.	105,106	107,108	109,110	111,112	113,114	115,116	117,118	119,120	121,122
37	J.Ph.	[7] 9,10	11,12	13,14	15,16	17,18	19,20	21,22	23,24	25,26
38	J.P.C.	18	19	20	21	22	23	24	25	26
39	J.Prak.	[2] 89,90	91,92	93,94	95,96	97,98	99	100	101-104	104,105
40	ψ	46	47	48	49	-	51	50,52	53	-
41	J.S.C.I.	33	34	35	36	37	38	39	40	41
42	Monat.	35	36	37	38	39	40	41	42	43
43	Nat.	92-94	94-96	96-98	98-100	100-102	102-104	104-106	106-108	108-110
44	O.S.								1	2
46	Phil.M.	[6] 27,28	29,30	31,32	33,34	35,36	37,38	39,40	41,42	43,44
47	Phil.T.	213,214	215,216	216,217	217	217				
48	P.R.	[2] 3,4	5,6	7,8	9,10	11,12	13,14	15,16	17,18	19,20
50	P.Soc.	30[15]	Subsequent issues do not contain scientific communications.							
51	P.Roy.S.	89,90	91	92	93	94	95	96,97	98,99	100,101
52	Rec.	33	34	35	36,37	37	38	39	40	41
53	Sitz.	123	124	125	126	127	128	129	130	131
54	Z.Anal.C.	53	54	55	56	57	58	59	60	61
55	Z.Ang.C.	27	28	29	30	31	32	33	34	35
56	Z.Anorg.	84-89	90-93	94-98	99-101	102-104	105-108	109-114	115-119	120-125
57	Z.El.C.	20	21	22	23	24	25	26	27	28
58	Z.Kryst.	53	54	-	-	-	-	55	-	56
59	Z.φ.X.	86-88	89,90	91	-	93	93	94-96	97-99	100-102
60	Z.Ph.C.	88-92	93-95	96,97	98-100	101-103	104-107	108-111	112-117	118-123

No.	Name	1923	1924	1925	1926	1927	1928	1929	1930	1931
2	A.J.S.	[5] 5,6	7,8	9,10	11,12	13,14	15,16	17,18	19,20	21,22
3	Anal.	48	49	50	51	52	53	54	55	56
4	Ann.	430-434	435-440	441-445	446-450	451-459	460-467	468-476	477-484	485-491
6&7	Ann.C.P.	[9] 19,20	[10] 1,2	3,4	5,6	7,8	9,10	11,12	13,14	15,16
8	Ann.M.	3,4	5,6	7,8	9,10	11,12	13,14	15,16	17,18	19,20
9	Ar.P.P.	[12] 96-100	101-104	105-110	111-118	119-126	127-138	138-146	147-158	159-162
10	A.P.	261	Vol. No.	abandoned in 1924;	citation henceforth by year and page.					
11	Atti.	[5] 32	33	[6]1,2	3,4	5,6	7,8	9,10	11,12	13,14
12	Bei.H.	5,6	-	7,8	9	10	11	12	13	14
13	Bei.E l.						1	2-4	5	6-8
16	Ber.	56	57	58	59	60	61	62	63	64
17	Bio.J.	17	18	19	20	21	22	23	24	25
18	Bio.Z.	134-143	144-154	155-166	167-179	180-191	192-203	204-216	217-229	230-243
19	Bull.	33,34	35,36	37,38	39,40	41,42	43,44	45,46	47,48	49,50
20	C.N.	126,127	128,129	130,131	132,133	134,135	136,137	138,139	140,141	142,143
21	C.Rev.			1,2	2,3	4	5	6	7	8,9
22	C.T.J.	72,73	74,75	76,77	78,79	80,81	82,83	84,85	86,87	88,89
24	C.W.	20	21	22	23	24	25	26	27	28
25	C.Ztg.	47	48	49	50	51	52	53	54	55
26	C.R.	176,177	178,179	180,181	182,183	184,185	186,187	188,189	190,191	192,193
27	D.P.J.	338	339	340	341	342	343	344	345	346*
29	Gazz.	53	54	55	56	57	58	59	60	61
30	A.Phys.	[4] 70-72	73-75	76-78	79-81	82-84	85-87	[5]1-3	4-7	8-11
31	I.E.C.	15	16	17	18	19	20	21	22	23
32	Helv.	6	7	8	9	10	11	12	13	14
33	J.A.C.S.	45	46	47	48	49	50	51	52	53
34	J.B.C.	55-57	58-61	62-66	67-71	72-75	76-80	81-84	85-89	90-93

* Ceased.

No.		1923	1924	1925	1926	1927	1928	1929	1930	1931
					Vol. No. abandoned in 1926; cited by year only.					
35	J.	123,124	125,126	127,128[3]	[8]1,2	3,4	5,6	7,8	9,10	11,12
37	J.Ph.	[7] 27,28	29,30							
38	J.P.C.	27	28	29	30	31	32	33	34	35
39	J.Prak.	[2] 106	107,108	109-111	112-114	115-117	118,119	120-123	124-128	129-131
40	ψ	–	54,55	56,57	58	59	60	61	62	1(63)[12]
41	J.S.C.I.	42	43	44	45	46	47	48	49	50
42	Monat.	44	45	46	47	48	49,50	51-54	55,56	57,58
43	Nat.	110-112	112-114	114-116	116-118	118-120	121,122	123,124	125,126	127,128
44	O.S.	3	4	5	6	7	8	9	10	11
46	Phil.M.	[6] 45,46	47,48	49,50	[7]1,2	3,4	5,6	7,8	9,10	11,12
47	Phil.T.									
48	P.R.	[2] 21,22	23,24	25,26	27,28	29,30	31,32	33,34	35,36	37,38
51	P.Roy.S.	102-104	105,106	107-109	110-112	113-116	117-121	122-125	126-129	130-133
52	Rec.	42	43	44	45	46	47	48	49	50
53	Sitz.	132	133	134	135	136	137	138	139	140
54	Z.Anal.C.	62,63	64	65,66	67-69	70-72	73-75	76-78	79-82	83-86
55	Z.Ang.C.	36	37	38	39	40	41	42	43	44
56	Z.Anorg.	126-131	132-141	142-149	150-158	159-167	168-176	177-184	185-194	195-202
57	Z.El.C.	29	30	31	32	33	34	35	36	37
58	Z.Kryst.	57,58	59,60	61,62	63,64	65	66-68	69-71	72-75	76-80
59	Z.φ.X. [A]	103-107	108-113	114-118	119-124	125-130	131-139	140-145	146-151	152-157
	Z.φ.X. [B]						1	2-6	7-10	11-14
60	Z.Ph.C.	124-131	132-141	142-150	151-161	162-172	173-179	180-185	186-193	194-203

No.	Name	1932	1933	1934	1935	1936	1937	1938	1939	1940
2	A.J.S.	[5] 23,24	25,26	27,28	29,30	31,32	33,34[9]	236	237	238
3	Anal.	57	58	59	60	61	62	63	64	65
4	Ann.	492-499	500-507	508-514	515-520	521-526	527-532	533-536	537-542	543-545
6&7	Ann.C.P.	[10] 17,18	19,20	[11] 1,2	3,4	5,6	7,8	9,10	11,12	13,14
8	Ann.M.	[13] 1,2	3,4	5,6	7,8	9,10	11,12	13,14	15,16	17,18
9	Ar.P.P.	163-168	169-173	174-176	177-179	180-183	184-186	187-190	191-194	195,196
11	Atti.	15,17	17,18	19,20	21,22	23,24	25,26	27	[7][4]1	2
12	Bei.H.	15	16,17	18,19	20-22	23-25	26,27	28a,30,31	28b,29a	29b
13	Bei.El.	9,10	{11+12, 13+14}	15+16	17+18+19	20+21+22	23+24+25	26+27	-	-
16	Ber.	65	66	67	68	69	70	71	72	73
17	Bio.J.	26	27	28	29	30	31	32	33	34
18	Bio.Z.	244-256	257-267	268-274	275-282	283-288	288-294	295-299	300-303	304-308
19	Bull.	[4] 51,52	53,54	[5] 1	2	3	4	5	6	7
20	C.N.	144,145[7]	Ceased publication in its original form.							
21	C.Rev.	10,11	12,13	14,15	16,17	18,19	20,21	22,23	24,25	26,27
22	C.T.J.	90,91	92,93	94,95	96,97	98,99	100,101	102,103	104,105	106,107
24	C.W.	29	30	31	32	33	34	35	36	37
25	C.Ztg.	56	57	58	59	60	61	62	63	64
26	C.R.	194,195	196,197	198,199	200,201	202,203	204,205	206,207	208,209	210,211
29	Gazz.	62	63	64	65	66	67	68	69	70
30	A.Phys.	[5] 12-15	16-18	19-21	23,24	25-27	28-30	31-33	34-36	37-39
31	I.E.C.	24	25	26	27	28	29	30	31	32
32	Helv.	15	16	17	18	19	20	21	22	23
33	J.A.C.S.	54	55	56	57	58	59	60	61	62
34	J.B.C.	94-98	99-103	104-107	108-111	112-116	117-121	122-126	127-131	132-136
36	J.O.C.					1	2	3	4	5

#	Journal		1932	1933	1934	1935	1936	1937	1938	1939	1940
37	J.Ph.	[8]	15,16	17,18	19,20	21,22	23,24	25,26	27,28	29,30	[9] 1
38	J.P.C.		36	37	38	39	40	41	42	43	44
39	J.Prak.		132-135	136-138	139-141	142,143	144-146	147-149	150,151	152,153	154-156
40	Z.Ob.K.		2(64)	3(65)	4(66)	5(67)	6(68)	7(69)	8(70)	9(71)	10(72)
41	J.S.C.I.		51	52	53	54	55	56	57	58	59
42	Monat.		59-61	62	63,64	65,66	67-69	70	71	72	73
43	Nat.		129,130	131,132	133,134	135,136	137,138	139,140	141,142	143,144	145,146
44	O.S.		12	13	14	15	16	17	18	19	20
46	Phil.M.	[7]	13,14	15,16	17,18	19,20	21,22	23,24	25,26	27,28	29,30
47	Phil.I.										
48	P.R.	[2]	39-42	43,44	45,46	47,48	49,50	51,52	53,54	55,56	57,58
51	P.Roy.S.		134-138	139-142	143-147	148-152	153-157	158-163	164-168	169-173	174-178
52	Rec.		51	52	53	54	55	56	57	58	59
53	Sitz.		141	142	143	144	145	146	147	148	149
54	Z.Anal.C.		87-90	91-95	96-99	100-103	104-107	108-110	111-114	115-117	118,119
55	Z.Ang.C.[19]		45	46	47	48	49	50	51	52	53
56	Z.Anorg.		203-209	210-215	216-220	221-225	226-229	230-234	235-239	240-242	243-245
57	Z.El.C.		38	39	40	41	42	43	44	45	46
58	Z.Kryst.		81-83	84-86	87-89	90-92	94-95	96,97	98,99	100-102	103
59	Z.φ.X.	[A]	158-162	163-167	168-170	171-174	175-177	178-180	181,182	183-185	186-
		[B]	15-19	20-23	24-27	28-30	31-34	35-37	38-41	42-44	45-
60	Z.Ph.C.		204-213	214-222	223-230	231-237	238-244	245-250	251-256	257-261	262-

No.	Name	1941	1942	1943	1944	1945	1946	1947	1948	1949
2	A.J.S.	239	240	241	242	243	244	245	246	247
3	Anal.	66	67	68	69	70	71	72	73	74
4	Ann.	546-549	550-553	554,555	556	557	-	558	559-561	562-565
6&7	Ann.C.P.	[11] 15,16	17	18	19	20	[12] 1	2	3	4
8	Ann.M.	[13] 19,20	[14] 1,2	2/132^6	133	134	135			
9	Ar.P.P.	197,198	199,200	201,202	203,204	-	-	204	205,206	207,208
11	Atti.	[7] 3	4	5	-	-	[8] 1	2,3	4,5	6,7
14	Bei.F2.	1	2-4	5	6	-	-	-	7,8	9,10
16	Ber.	74	75	76	77	-	-	80^5	81	82
17	Bio.J.	35	36	37	38	39	40	41	42,43	44,45
18	Bio.Z.	309-310	311-313	314-316	317	-	-	-	318	-
19	Bull.	[5] 8	9	10	11	12	Vol. No. subsequently dropped.			
21	C.Rev.	28,29	30,31	32,33	34,35	36,37	38,39	40,41^8	42,43	44,45
22	C.T.J.	108,109	110,111	112,113	114,115	116,117	118,119	120,121	122,123	124,125
24	C.W.	38	39	40	-	41^{16}	42	43	44	45
25	C.Ztg.	65	66	67	68	69	70	71	72	73
26	C.R.	212,213	214,215	216,217	218,219	220,221	222,223	224,225	226,227	228,229
29	Gazz.	71	72	73	74	75	76	77	78	79
30	A.Phys.	[5] 39,40	41,42	43,44	45,46	47,48	49,50	[6] 1,2	3,4	5,6
31	I.E.C.	33	34	35	36	37	38	39	40	41
32	Helv.	24	25	26	27	28	29	30	31	32
33	J.A.C.S.	63	64	65	66	67	68	69	70	71
34	J.B.C.	137-141	142-146	147-151	152-156	157-161	162-166	167-171	172-176	177-181

	1941	1942	1943	1944	1945	1946	1947	1948	1949
36 J.O.C.	6	7	8	9	10	11	12	13	14
37 J.Ph.	[9]	Merged with Bull. Sci. Pharmacol. as Ann. Pharm. Franc.							
38 J.P.C.	45	46	47	48	49	50	51	52	53
39 J.Prak.	158,159	159,160	161,162[11]	Continued as J. Makromolekular Chemie.					
40 Z.Ob.C.	11(73)	12(74)	13(75)	14(76)	15(77)	16(78)	17(79)	18(80)	19(81)
41 J.S.C.I.	60	61	62	63	64	65	66	67	68
42 Monat:		74							
43 Nat.	147,148	149,150	151,152	153,154	155,156	157,158	159,160	161,162	163,164
44 O.S.	21	22	23	24	25	26	27	28	29
46 Phil.M.	[7[31,32	33	34	35	36	37	38	39	40
47 Phil.T.					—	239	240	241	241,242
48 P.R.	59,60	61,62	63,64	65,66	67,68	69,70	71,72	73,74	75,76
52 Rec.	60	61	62	63	64	65	66	67	68
54 Z.Anal.C.	120,121	122,123	124,125	126,127	—	—	128(I)	128(II&III)	129,130
55 Ang.C.	54	55	56	57	—	—	59	60	61
56 Z.Anorg.C.	246-248	249,250	251,252	252	253		254	255,256	257-260
57 Z.El.C.	47	48	49	50	51		52		53

No.	Name	1950	1951	1952	1953	1954	1955	1956
2	A.J.S.	248	249	250	251	252	253	254
3	Anal.	75	76	77	78	79	80	81
4	Ann.	566-570	571-574	575-578	579-584	585-590	591-597	598-604
6&7	Ann.C.P.	[12] 5	6	7	8	9	10	11
9	Ar.P.P.	209-211	212-214	215-217	218-220	221-223	224-226	227-229
11	Atti.	[8] 8,9	10,11	12,13	14,15	16,17	18,19	20,21
14	Bei.E2.	11-13	14-16	17-19	20-22	23-26	27-Index (Pt. I)	Index (Pt. II)
16	Ber.5	83	84	85	86	87	88	89
17	Bio.J.	46,47	48,49	50-52	53-55	56-58	59-61	62-64
21	C.Rev.	46,47	48,49	50,51	52,53	54	55	56
22	C.T.J.	126,127	128,129	130,131	132,133	134,135	136,137	138
24	C.W.	46	47	48	49	50	51	52
25	C.Ztg.	74	75	76	77	78	79	80
26	C.R.	230,231	232,233	234,235	236,237	238,239	240,241	242
29	Gazz.	80	81	82	83	84	85	86
30	A.Phys.	[6] 7,8	9,10	11,12	13,14	15,16	17,18	19
31	I.E.C.	42	43	44	45	46	47	48
32	Helv.	33	34	35	36	37	38	39
33	J.A.C.S.	72	73	74	75	76	77	78
34	J.B.C.	182-187	188-193	194-199	200-205	206-211	212-217	218-223
36	J.O.C.	15	16	17	18	19	20	21
38	J.P.C.	54	55	56	57	58	59	60

	1950	1951	1952	1953	1954	1955	1956
40 Z.Ob.K.	20(82)	21(83)	22(84)	23(85)	24	25	26
41 J.S.C.I.	69	1[23]	2	3	4	5	6
42 Monat.	81	82	83	84	85	86	87
43 Nat.	165,166	167,168	169,170	171,172	173,174	175,176	177
44 O.S.	30	31	32	33	34	35	36
47 Phil.T.	242,243	243,244	244,245	245,246	246,247	247,248	248,249
48 P.R.	77-80	81					
52 Rec.	69	70	71	72	73	74	75
54 A.Anal.C.	130,131	132-134	134-137	137-140	141-143	144-148	148-
55 Ang.C.	62	63	64	65	66	67	68
56 Z.Anorg.[24]	260-263	264-267	267-271	271-273	274-277	278-282	283-286

NOTES ON APPENDIX III

1. After Vol. 150 [2nd Series] the **Archiv der Pharmazie** was numbered serially, as from the commencement of Series [1]. There is, therefore, a gap between Vols. 150 and 201. Part of Vol. 201 appeared in 1872.

2. The **Annales de Chimie** had as its original title **Annales de Chimie, ou Recueil de memoires concernant la Chimie et les arts qui en dependent,** to which was added in 1800 (with Vol. 33) **et specialement la pharmacie.** Three special indexes were published in 1801, 1807 and 1821.

3. Certain journals, such as the **Journal of The Chemical Society, Archiv der Pharmazie** etc., decided to dispense with volume numbers and to use the year number for the identification of volumes.

4. In 1939 the **Archiv der Pharmacie** was absorbed in **Union Pharmaceutique.**

5. As **Chemische Berichte** resumed publication with the serial number 80, in 1947.

6. In 1943 the name was changed to **Annales des Mines et des carburants,** and the volume number replaced by a number indicating the number of years the journal has been in existence.

7. **The Chemical News,** as a medium for the publication of original communications, ceased in 1932; it has been resuscitated as **Chemical Products and Chemical News** but in a somewhat different form.

8. A collective author and subject index to **Chemical Reviews** Vols. 1-40 has been issued.

9. The series number of the **American Journal of Science** was dropped in 1938, and the 'total volume number' used thereafter.

10. **Gilbert's Annalen** started in 1799 (Vols. 1-3). It was the lineal descendant of the **Journal der Physik** (1790-1794; 8 vols.) and of the **Neues Journal der Physik** (1794-1798; 4 vols.).

11. **J.Pr.Chem.** ceased in 1943 and was continued as the **Journal für Makromolekular Chemie.**

12. **J. Russ. Phys. Chem. Soc.** became **Journal of General Chemistry** (U.S.S.R.) (Zhurnal Obshchei Khimii), in 1931.

13. **Nicholson's Journal (A Journal of Natural Philosophy, Chemistry and the Arts)** has the record:-

1797-1801   5 Vols.
1802-1813   36 Vols.

It was then merged with the **Philosophical Magazine** (1814). The latter was founded in 1798.

14. Publication of the **Phil. Trans.** dates from 1665, and it was the first scientific (as opposed to purely chemical) journal. The journal is issued in two separate series, that marked A being for the Mathematical and Physical Sciences; that of B serving the Biological Sciences. In the preceding tables only Series A is entered.

15. Since 1915 no scientific matter is published in these **Proceedings.**

16. **Chemisch Weekblad** ceased publication in May 1943, and resumed in August 1945; thus, there is no volume for 1944.

17. The first publications of the Chemical Society were **Memoirs** and **Proceedings** in 1843, issued separately but usually bound together. The two subsequent volumes, entitled **Memoirs and Proceedings,** and issued together, cover 1843-1845 and 1845-1847; the **Journal** proper commenced in 1847, as a **Quarterly Journal,** the word **Quarterly** being dropped in 1862.

18. **Z. Anal. Chem.** is often referred to in early citations as **Fresenius' Journal,** after its first editor.

19. **Z. Angewandte Chemie** has had several minor changes of title; in 1932 it was changed to **Angewandte Chemie;** in 1942 to **Die Chemie,** but in 1945 the former title of **Angewandte Chemie** was restored.

20. During the second world war, a number of journals temporarily ceased publication, and others were sent out in attenuated form; this is reflected in the tables by the gaps after 1940.

21. To enable the tables to be printed within the compass of the page certain journals whose volume number is entirely regular are omitted; chief among them are:-

    1. **Trans. Faraday Society,** Vol. 1, 1905.
    2. **Journal of Chemical Education,** Vol. 1, 1924.

Journal of Chemical Physics, Vol. 1, 1933.

22. The **Abstract Journals** are not shewn in the tables, as in the case of **British Abstracts** and **Chemisches Centralblatt** citation is by year alone; with **Chemical Abstracts** the volume number has been entirely regular since the commencement in 1907.

23. The **Journal of the Society of Chemical Industry** was replaced in 1951 by the **Journal of Applied Chemistry**, starting with Vol. 1.

24. The **Zeitschrift für anorganische Chemie** changed its name by the addition of 'und allgemeine' before 'Chemie' in 1915; in August 1943 it changed back to the shorter title – in 1950, however, it changed again to **Zeitschrift für anorganische und allgemeine Chemie** – where it remains at the moment.

AUTHOR INDEX

SUBJECT INDEX